#43

Dedicated to the beacon of my life, my darling wife, Kathleen, and the heartbeats of my life, my son, Luke and the little one on the way. Thank you for always being there, thank you for being you, for me.

GEORGIA,

WISHING YOU AND THE FAMILY HEALTH, HAPPINESS AND CONTINUED SUCCESS WITH YOUR RUNNERS.

I HOPE YOU ENJOY THE

BOOK.

I WILL NEVER FORGET BOSTON '96!

RUN TALL, RUN EASY....

YOUR FRIEND,

COACH GP

04/10/04

Published by Great Performance Coaching & Conditioning
Printed in the United States of America
Printed and bound by Book-Mart Press, Inc. New Jersey

Library of Congress Cataloging-in-Publication Data
Pearlberg, Gerard.
Run Tall Run Easy: The Ultimate Guide to Better Running / GP
Pearlberg; Foreword by Eddy Hellebuyck.

1st paperback ed.
        p.   cm.

ISBN 0-9706120-5-2
SAN 254-2641
1. Running – Training. 2. Exercise. I. Title.

Questions regarding the content of this book should be addressed to
        Running Buzz.com
        310 Green Avenue
        Brielle, N.J. 08730
        www.runningbuzz.com
        email: coachgp@runningbuzz.com

Cover photo (Coach GP) by Seraphina Landgrebe seraphina.com
Cover photo (Barb Acosta #1) by Marathon Foto marathonfoto.com
Strength-training photography by Dennis Stehle
Book cover design, book production and layout by Nicole Olds

Run Tall, Run Easy.

The Ultimate Guide to Better Running Mechanics

How to run:

Faster...

Longer...

Easier...

Here are your splits...

Foreword

Speaking as the current Masters champion and a professional runner of many years, believe me it is not often that you come across a new perspective in the sport of distance running. Nevertheless Coach GP has just that – a new perspective on how to be a better runner – a perspective that is contained within the pages of this book.

For several years now Coach GP has been my friend, professional colleague and business partner. While attending a recent marathon in South Carolina, I told GP just how much I have gained from his innovative workouts and his unique approach to running biomechanics. We Masters competitors no longer enjoy the magical benefits and speedy recovery times of our youth. We are forced to focus on both the cardiovascular and the biomechanical aspects of our bodies just to stay in the game.

GP began his running career as a mid-pack runner at the 1990 New York City marathon, finishing in 4 hours and 41 minutes. Over the next eight years, he improved his time in the marathon by over two hours, and reduced his mile time from 10 minutes to 4 minutes and 21 seconds at age 35. In this book GP clearly explains the secrets behind his remarkable journey. He takes a unique look at nutrition and its effect on exercise. He also offers advice on those strength-training exercises that will best help you in your quest to improve your running. Above all, GP addresses a much overlooked and undervalued aspect of our sport, that being running biomechanics.

As GP convincingly argues, volumes have been written and many hours dedicated to improving our golf or tennis swing, but we have invested almost no time in the improvement of the way we run. He deals with the critical aspects of running "form" in a convincing and engaging manner, providing "form" in a convincing and engaging manner, providing straightforward tips that will have an immediate and positive impact on your running. What's more, you will find that GP's expertise bears equal relevance for all runners regardless of age, shape, size or speed.

Just as this book will be an invaluable resource both in my own training as a professional runner and also when training athletes in my capacity as a professional coach, Run Tall, Run Easy will undoubtedly help you to maximize your full running potential!

Eddy Hellebuyck
1996 Olympic marathoner
USA Masters Champion

GP's Basic Laws of Running

1. Establish a rhythm.
2. Run under control/within yourself.
3. Establish good biomechanics (foot strike, heel recovery, flight phase, support phase, arm/carriage).
4. Maintain good range of motion and flexibility in the joints and muscles through active isolated stretching.
5. Do not go too fast/far too soon.
6. Establish accurate, obtainable goals.
7. Wear good shoes.

GP's Philosophy of Running

1. Running is the oldest purest sport known to mankind.
2. No apparatus or machinery required.
3. It's the anytime, anywhere, put-on-your-shoes-and-head-out-the-door kind of sport, a natural blend of art and science.
4. Running when performed properly is poetry in motion. It is the simple task of moving your body across the face of the earth as efficiently and effortlessly as possible.
5. Running brings improved health and quality of life, an endorphin-induced natural high.

The Warm-Up:
Turnover and Flight

-
-
-
-

As runners, whether recreational or competitive, we are inundated with information regarding heart rate training. Indeed, cardiovascular workouts and performance represent a key component to success in any runner's training and racing program. However, there is another component that until now has been largely overlooked: the runner's biomechanical form. As a runner you may have always suspected this was important but perhaps didn't know exactly what you could do about it and so let your suspicions pass. But there is something you can do! In fact, as I have discovered through my coaching and my continued research, there are many things you can do to change and improve the way you run. So, it is now my mission, through the writing of this book, to help you improve your running biomechanics so that you are always running to your full ability. We are going to take a look at how you actually run.

Consider heart rate training and increased cardiopulmonary performance in terms of "improving a car's engine." Taking the analogy a little further, if a car's engine is upgraded to a more powerful version, it will be maximally effective only if the chassis, transmission and drive shaft are upgraded at the same time. So it is with running. All of the cardiovascular training methods are excellent for improving the runner's heart and lungs (engine), but somewhat redundant if the runner has poor biomechanics (chassis, drive shaft and transmission). It is this aspect of running that is so much neglected, to the detriment of thousands of runners.

In the following pages you will find that there are two principal factors that remain constant in terms of efficient running biomechanics. We'll be examining these factors closely. They are:

1. How fast your feet are moving, i.e., "turnover"

2. How much distance you generate during flight: known as the "flight phase"

Several of the chapters will conclude with one key element that you can use as a physical and psychological tool to tuck away in your memory banks. During your runs, you can use these tools to help you get out of difficulties such as fatigue, shortness of breath and mental anguish.

I will also be discussing the concept of training with purpose and self-motivation as opposed to mindless exercising without direction or strategy, a practice that all too often leads to disappointment for runners trying to achieve their fitness goals. This path to a more positive and successful approach to all of your fitness goals can be found in the chapter entitled "Don't Exercise...Train!"

In our final chapter, "Run Tall, Run Easy: Getting out of Trouble," we will conclude with my "Fab Four" - the very best ways I know for you to tough out your particularly difficult runs and races.

The word "runner" will be mentioned *ad infinitum* in this book in the third person. At the risk of offending one gender or another, with the exception of "Joe" and for the express purpose of simplification, all runners will be assumed to be female.

Remember, as runners, we are "ordinary people doing extraordinary things."

Enjoy and happy running and reading.

Coach GP

Mile 1.0
The Child at Play

•

•

•

•

In a wonderfully written book called "Racing the Antelope" by Professor Bernd Heinrich, the reader is challenged to consider the antelope as the ultimate long distance running machine. Possessing an abundance of grace and effortless athleticism, this animal thrives on its natural instincts of survival and its ability to continue to run as an adult with the same wonderful mechanics that it was blessed with as a fawn.

As a child growing up in England in the late 60's and 70's, I lived in a society not yet suffering the affliction of music videos, computers and video games. My natural instinct, after returning home from school, was to get outside and play football (soccer). Of course my parents were trying very hard to get me to do my homework, but who had time for that? So, there I was calling up my friends and arranging "very serious" games of pick-up soccer or hide and seek. We would be outside for hours, running around like crazy, having the time of our young lives...and in the south of England, it should be added, we played in all types of weather.

Biologically speaking, a child at play represents nature's natural order. It is the method we human beings use to develop our agility, coordination, awareness of our surroundings and kinesiology.

Of course, the last thing I thought about at eight years old, was that some 30 years later I would be writing a book, discussing how as a child playing soccer, I was really developing my kinesiology. Back then all I wanted to do was win the game, go home cold, wet and happy, then sit down to a great grub up (supper) and tell my dad all about it.

Mile 2.0
The Child Runs Tall

•

•

•

•

As children we benefit from not having had to fight gravity for very long. Over a period of years however, this same fight takes its toll on the body and as you can see from observing older generations, it contributes to compromised posture.

As children, we physically run around at our "maximum height". If we are 4 feet 2 inches, we play to the height of 4 feet 2 inches, with our spinal discs evenly spaced, our upper leg muscles developing and flexible, our gluteus muscles (buttocks) strong. Also for the most part (although there are exceptions) active children do not carry excessive amounts of body fat, as compared to adults. This means that for many people, their power-to-weight ratios are better at this early stage in their lives, than in any subsequent stage. From a runner's perspective in particular, this is not good news.

In the chapters to come I will attempt to unravel the mysteries of poor biomechanics and how they may be overcome. I will strive to provide you with sometimes humorous, but always useful information. I will give you the knowledge that will enable you to return to playful running -- relaxed running with good posture. I will focus on several changes that you can make which will have an immediate and permanent positive impact on your running.

▪▪▪

Mile 3.0
The Story of Joe...a Child No More

-

-

-

-

As runners, the story of Joe is one with which we can easily identify. You see, Joe is the "weekend warrior" personified, outwardly confident, game for many things. On a challenge from a friend, he has been training for a local 10K for about three weeks. The good news is that he has been training (termed loosely). The bad news is that the 10K is this weekend. He feels that this poses no problem, as many people similarly would. He thinks to himself, "I used to be an athlete in college. How hard could it be to run six miles?"

On the morning of the race, Joe is ready to go. He drives to the start, gets out of his car, lifts his bent leg onto the bumper for a quick hamstring stretch and does a 60-second warm-up jog. Now, Joe is ready to race, or so he thinks.

Joe is psyched to see that his wife and children are there, along with his friends, none of whom can believe he took up the dare in the first place. He nervously chugs down half a bottle of his favorite sports drink, takes a bite of his friend's energy bar, bobs up and down in an attempt to touch his toes and awaits the start. The gun goes off and the race begins...

A half mile into the race, Joe is looking pretty good, except for the fact that he is running one-mile race pace in a 10K, a mistake that will later come back to haunt him. However, that notwithstanding, he is using all of his 5 feet 10 inch frame, is pumping his arms and has good leg turnover.

O.K., at this point, I will leave Joe a half-mile into his 10K. We'll return to his story a little later...

Mile 4.0
The Planet...The Taller You Are

-
-
-
-

I mentioned in my opening chapter that the older we get, the longer we have been fighting gravity just to remain upright. As can plainly be seen in older generations, this challenge can take its toll over time. In later years it can single-handedly lead to poor posture with flexion in the shoulders and rounding in the back. In effect, we'll have gotten closer to the planet.

Runners are prone to the very same phenomenon. The closer we become to the planet relative to our own height, the worse things become in our running form and efficiency. Conversely the taller we remain relative to our height, the better our body will fare and the more efficient we will be.

Forward lean

One of the first characteristics in the breakdown of running form is the tendency to lean forward. Why should this be? Well, let's examine this more closely.

There are 206 bones in the human body. These bones are at their most efficient in the fight against gravity when they are perfectly stacked upon one another, much as you would find on a skeletal diagram. Remember as a child, trying to balance mom's broomstick or mop on one finger? It was a fun thing to do and of much annoyance to your poor old mom. When you held the broomstick perpendicular to the ground, very little effort was required to maintain the position.

Demonstration of the "Broomstick" principle.

Did you happen to notice how much more energy it took to try to hold that broom in place if the broomstick was to move from its upright position and you tried to stop it from hitting the ground?

The same holds true with running. The more forward lean you establish, especially if that lean is established from the waist, the greater the additional stress that will be applied to the area of support and stability (i.e., the low back and pelvic area, the foundation of your torso). When leaning forward, you are basically spending more energy than is necessary during the course of your run.

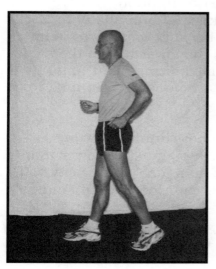

Photo shows both the proper alignment of the shoulders over the hips and the proper alignment of the hips over the lower body.

Pelvic rotation

That is not all. If you are leaning forward you will soon have a second problem to deal with. I am referring to restricted hip movement. When you lean too far forward, either from the hip or the waist (waist is worse), you will almost certainly experience too much anterior rotation of your pelvis.

To simplify matters, think of the pelvis as a bucket of water. Now imagine holding that bucket of water out in front of you nice and steady. Anterior rotation could be imagined as pouring that bucket of water away from you in a forward fashion (the front of the bucket dropping and the back of the bucket rising closest to you). Conversely, posterior rotation could be imagined as pouring the bucket of water over yourself.

Now, if your hips are in anterior rotation, you are restricting the upper leg's (knee to hip) ability to swing forward and through because your torso is in the way. This then prevents the lower half of the same leg from reaching out and maximizing flight time. By leaning too far forward you are no longer running to your full height.

Logically speaking, if you're not running to your maximum height, then your hips must be lower than ideal. If your hips are lower than ideal, your body will now have to rise up and over your foot after it lands.

Demonstration of hips being set too low.

During the running cycle, your leg swings through and your foot lands. Now your torso moves over that foot and the foot pushes off, thus starting the cycle all over again. However, if, once the foot lands, the lead or front leg is overly bent and too far out in front of the body, your trunk and hips will sink unnecessarily low before starting the next leg cycle. This causes you to have to "lift up" against gravity at the same time as trying to propel your body forward. Consider this -- over the course of a 5K race, if you have employed just five centimeters of excess vertical movement per stride, then in terms of wasted energy you will have added the equivalent of a run up a five-story building to the end of your run.

Remembering that with too much lean you are already restricting your travel in the air. Not only are you now wasting precious energy in forward motion (through running too low for your height) but you are also not going as far (through restricted leg motion due to anterior rotation of the hips caused by forward lean). As your form deteriorates you will go through this "up and over" process using excessive energy and losing ground with each step. If you multiply these two factors by your volume of foot strikes over distance, such as a mile, they become significant indeed.*

Shoulders and arms

Now if, as a runner, your hips are set too low, your body will naturally compensate through the raising of your shoulders and arms. Basically, your body will be doing its best to raise its center of gravity and your shoulders will be creeping up closer to your ears. If you observe runners as frequently as I do, this trait becomes very easy to spot and is more bad news for

---

* *Training Distance Runners, Coe/Martin 'Chapter 1'*

the poor old runner. Just why is it that this particular breakdown in form is such a negative? Again, we'll look at this a little further.

Some of the major back muscles that play an integral role in running and forward locomotion, are the large *latissimus dorsi* muscles that sit on either side of the spine. Sometimes referred to as the "wings of the back," these muscles are extremely powerful. The human muscular network tends to work on the "big brother principle" whereby given the opportunity to be engaged, the larger muscles will win out in the fight to perform a given task.

In order to clarify this point, let's move away from running for a moment, into in a gym setting. If a runner is in a gym to perform a strength workout, one of the popular back exercises is the One Arm, or Single Arm Row (see accompanying photos). This is usually completed with one hand resting on a bench along with the knee of the corresponding side. The other leg stands straight on the floor and slightly out to the side for better balance and a more stable platform from which to lift the weight. The runner will now lift the weight, usually a dumbbell, with the exercising arm. Now, in order to maximally engage the *latissimus dorsi* ("lats" or back muscles) thereby strengthening the back, the weight should be lifted in the direction of the hip. However, countless times I have seen this exercise performed incorrectly by athletes, lifting the weight too high up their bodies and more in line with their shoulders. This then almost entirely excludes the much more powerful lat muscles from assisting in the movement and generating power, leaving the task for the much smaller and weaker deltoids (shoulders) to complete.

Demonstration of correct (shown left) and incorrect (shown right) form when performing the "one-arm row." Note GP has substituted an exercise ball for the bench in this demonstration but the exercise remains the same.

Why include the explanation of the "one arm row" exercise at this point? Well, this exercise happens to parallel almost exactly what occurs when we runners raise our arms up too high along our torsos and our shoulders creep closer to our ears. We end up losing the sustained power of the large back muscles and replacing it with that of smaller, weaker muscles. These slow-twitch muscles, though enduring, cannot assist as much in locomotion over a long period of time and will restrict our ability to run over distance in a relaxed and efficient manner.

Don't forget

So, here are the three things to remember while you are out there running and racing. Keep your hips "neutral," keep your shoulders over your hips and keep as much space as possible between your shoulders and your ears.

This leads us to the first of my "Fab Four" guidelines, specific directions that you can use whenever trouble strikes...

FAB #1: Run Tall

At the first sign of fatigue, slowing down or diminishing form, remind yourself to raise up from the hips and "run tall."

Mile 5.0
Foot Strike

-
-
-
-

One of the greatest aspects of running is its repetitive contact with "Mother Earth."

Runners move at several miles per hour and each second or so, come into contact with the earth. In turn, the earth moves at several thousand miles per hour through space. Perhaps this unique combination goes some way towards explaining the amazing natural highs and feelings of exhilaration that can occur while we participate in our favorite sport, a sport that is freedom personified.

When running, your "ground mechanics" (the correct positioning of the lead leg and foot immediately before contact with the ground) play a critical role in the fluidity of forward motion and in the minimizing of impact forces.

Midfoot or heel strike?

Under normal running conditions, the only thing to come in contact with the ground is our feet, i.e., our foot strike, an intricate part of the leg cycle whose importance I cannot overstate. Quite simply, the more efficiently our foot strike is performed, the less time our feet spend on the ground. The less time our feet spend on the ground, the faster we can return the legs to the next leg cycle.

Furthermore, both the location (relative to your center of gravity or body position) and the angle at which our foot strikes the ground have a major impact on your efficiency to propel yourself forward.

The question of forefoot or midfoot strike versus heel strike can be somewhat controversial. We'll use a combination of common sense and cold hard facts to find the answer. First, allow me to state with emphasis that for many reasons that we'll discuss, I am a proponent of the former, that is to say the forefoot/ midfoot strike.

The shoe question

Too many coaches throughout the world focus exclusively on the cardio-pulmonary aspects of training, without taking the time at the high school, college and club levels, to actually teach runners how to run. Very often when I address a group of runners, I hear the following very valid question: "If the forefoot/ mid-foot strike is the proper technique to utilize when running, why is it that shoe manufacturers have focused all of their attention on the support at the heel base of the shoe?"

My answer is twofold. Historically the mass population of runners has developed poor habits through lack of available coaching. Poor technique has resulted in the majority of novice mid-pack runners evolving as heel-strikers. In order to accommodate this style of running, shoe manufacturers have historically focused on the heel counter of their shoes. I believe that the shoe industry as a whole could have done -- and can still do -- much more in the educational arena, teaching children how to run properly. They could certainly sponsor many more running camps at the high school and club levels. The expense involved would not be prohibitive and could potentially foster a long-term loyalty to the generous sponsor. Furthermore, the benefits for our children, along with the long-term prospects for track and field competition in the United States, would be tremendous.

Second, the truth is that shoe manufacturers have in fact begun to pay more attention to midfoot support, cushioning and stability in recent years.

What's wrong with the heel-first strike?

Earlier in this book, we discussed "a child at play." If a child were running barefoot in a park or on a beach, she would not be striking the ground heel-first. She would in fact be landing on her midfoot, demonstrating simply but clearly that the heel-first strike is not the optimal biomechanical method of running for our biped species.

In the previous chapter, we concluded that the taller you remain relative to your own height, the more efficiently and effectively you will be able to run. Now, when landing as a heel striker, you must land with your foot positioned significantly out in front of your body. In fact, you land with your front leg bent to such an extent that it forces you to drop your hips. Once again, in order to propel your body forward, you have to first rise up and over the front foot in order to be able to extend your hip. The net result? A constant fight with gravity and a continual waste of precious energy.

Photograph again showing the hips set too low with the lead foot too far out in front of the athlete's center of gravity.

Further negative effects are felt by virtue of the angle that your front foot now drives into the ground, causing excessive shock and undue stress up through the lower leg muscles and knee joints and into the sacral pelvic floor.

The beginning of the next leg cycle is considerably slower than with the midfoot strike since the forward moving torso (carriage) first has to catch up with the front foot, before the drive-off leg is in a position to push off. Additionally, the angle of the flexed front foot causes a roll-over effect as the runner moves through the heel, to the toe and then to the push-off, slowing down the process even more.

Once the torso (carriage) is in the position to be driven forward again by the propulsion of the back leg (due to the fact that the hips are set too low), the back leg again has to drive the hips and upper body up as well as forward. Due to the slow nature of the whole movement, significant drive-off power is lost.

What happens with the midfoot strike?

Alternatively, with the midfoot strike, the support leg is straighter, the torso is moving forward faster and the drive-off leg action is more powerful. The only requirement then is for the hips to be driven forward. When used in conjunction with good arm and powerful leg drives (as will be discussed in Miles 7 and 8) the midfoot or forefoot strike provides for a faster, smoother running technique that reduces impact forces and allows for better shock absorption (in particular aiding runners with certain preexisting back and knee conditions). It also provides a faster transition back into the leg cycle and creates better posture and a more relaxed running position.

Both photographs show the proper positioning for the front foot a split-second after its contact with the ground.

Most importantly these benefits apply across the board to runners of all shapes and sizes and levels of ability, from featherweight to Clydesdale and from novice to elite.

FAB #2: Foot Strike

Paying attention to where you strike the ground can significantly improve your running form and counter the effects of fatigue. With the midfoot/ forefoot strike, the whole running process is effective, efficient and fast!

Mile 6.0
Metronome

-

-

-

-

The laws of physics dictate that the closer a weight is to the point of axis, the faster that weight shall revolve through space around it. When I was a child learning to play piano, this was demonstrated to me by Mr. Fox, my wiry, gray haired old stick of a piano teacher. He used a metronome to keep me in tempo.

Simply stated, the metronome is an instrument that works on the pendulum principle, whereby the further you slide the weight up the scale away from the point of axis, the slower the pendulum will swing. Thus, the slower you are supposed to play in order to keep time, with the reverse applying if the weight is pushed closer to the point of axis. I used to have fun ignoring this particular law of physics, much to the annoyance of the aforementioned Mr. Fox, but that is a whole different story.

Now, back to the business at hand. Having visited the always useful metronome, you may well ask, "How is this connected to running?" In the biomechanics of running, the point of axis that I am referring to is the hip joint and the weight is the foot.

At the point of drive-off, the more speed generated, the swifter and more powerful the heel recovery is (the action of the foot/heel coming up towards the gluteus before swinging back through into the flight phase). Therefore, the closer the foot to the hips, (i.e., weight to the point of axis) the faster and more efficient this action will be.

Note position of trail leg relative to hip/glutes.

Also note angle of upper to lower arm, angle of upper to lower leg and angle of head.

Insofar as the principles of physics are related to the mechanics of running, it is critical that you remember the two key factors determining your speed. These are:

1:   How fast your legs are moving (turnover rate)

2:   The distance you travel with each stride.

Your flight phase (distance traveled in the air) is largely determined by the speed and force generated at drive-off and the subsequent speed and efficiency of the leg cycle (the action of the trail leg as it contracts up and swings through to become the lead leg in preparation for the support phase,) along with the individual's core strength. (*See Mile 12.0*)

With the heel-first strike, the leg is placed out in front of the body and it simply is not possible to generate the speed and power that can be attained with a midfoot strike. This is because the subsequent drive-off force is compromised and the weight remains further away from the point of axis through the leg cycle (foot to hip). The result is a slower, less efficient mode of running.

Conversely, with the midfoot strike you are landing "tall" and over your center of gravity. The drive-off force generated is faster and more powerful, promoting better heel recovery. This, then, results in a faster turnover and increased distance generated in flight, both of which we have identified as critical aspects of faster running.

Conclusion on heel recovery

The metronome analogy and its pendulum principle aptly demonstrate the importance of returning the supporting leg -- aided by the midfoot strike -- into the next leg cycle as quickly as possible, promoting improved heel recovery and generating speed.

Mile 7.0
The Horse and Jockey

-
-
-
-

There is a wonderful analogy in the annals of running history known as the "horse and jockey." The idea in the "horse and jockey" is that your body is comprised of two separate entities acting as one. The horse is represented by the lower body, from the hipbones down. The jockey is represented by the torso from the hip bones up.

Imagine for a moment, that a race horse could talk. (Work with me here). Weighing in at 1,000 lbs, she would be most unlikely to ask her 90-pound jockey to assist her in providing running power. Instead, the jockey is there to provide rhythm, tempo and direction. This is true of the runner to a large degree. We must receive our power from our "prime movers," which are our lower body muscles. The carriage (torso) provides stability, balance, rhythm, tempo and direction. The "jockey" must be positioned over the "horse" for optimum synergy and the carriage must remain atop the lower body with the shoulders properly aligned over the hips. In other words, the "jockey" must not be in danger of falling off the front or the rear of the "horse" by leaning too far forward or backward. The "jockey" should sit with excellent posture. Chest up, relaxed shoulders, head level and arms perfectly synchronized with the "horse."

The "horse and jockey" technique can be used in various ways to get out of trouble. For example, by simply focusing on these principles during tough moments in a run, you stay alert, in the present and in a positive mental state. By adjusting the intensities of arm drive and leg turnover, you can change your workload and gait patterns so that you can actually recruit muscles in a different way. This affords you precious moments of active recovery while you are still in motion.

Become a better "jockey" and you will become a better runner. Your "racehorse" will be particularly appreciative!

Mile 8.0
The Fighter Jet, the Crossbow and the Swimming Pool

- •

- •

- •

- •

For the purposes of discussion in this book, I hope you will allow me to make the assumption that my readers are interested in improving their running in a forward-moving direction. I am well aware that there are exceptions to this rule, runners who do off-the-wall things, such as circumventing the globe while running backwards. If you are a proponent of this style of running, then I would advise you to reverse all the principles that you read in this chapter!

In the previous chapter I made reference to the "horse and jockey." Now, I want to turn your attention to the jockey aspect of the analogy and look at the jockey in a little more detail.

The swimming pool and the fighter jet

From a biomechanical perspective, the jockey is where it all begins in the sport of running. In short, nothing happens until the jockey climbs upon the horse. The success or failure of a run (biomechanically speaking) can be attributed directly to the effectiveness of the runner in producing an adequate and sustained arm drive. If you were standing in a swimming pool chest high in water and thrust your arms behind you, in which direction would you be sent by the resulting force? The answer is forward, of course! Simple enough, but it is amazing how mixed the answers are when I ask a group of runners the same question.

Consider this: a fighter jet at the point of take-off on an aircraft carrier produces massive amounts of thrust in order to get airborne from a short runway. In which direction are the engines thrusting their power? The answer, of course, is in the opposite of the one in which the jet will be taking off. We are talking about take-off here, not landing. Thrust produced in any direction other than forward would be problematic indeed.

In physics there is a term known as the "hinge moment." There are many examples of hinge moment in athletics. Javelin, hammer and discus-throwing all have their version of hinge moment -- which can be understood as the point at which one force ceases and another force continues. One example would be the initiation of flight of a javelin, the hinge moment occurring at the point when the forward movement of the throwing arm stops and the javelin is released.

For runners, a hinge moment occurs when you drive your foot into the ground, Mother Earth says "No more," and thrusts your foot upwards again, returning it to the leg cycle. Your arm movement is in complete unison at all times with the leg of the corresponding side, driving in the opposite direction.

As previously mentioned, in running biomechanics, the second of the two key components is the distance you travel with each stride. Maximal flight time can be achieved only with optimal arm drive, hence the importance of the jockey in running. The fighter jet and swimming pool principles are offered here to convey the importance of counterthrust (arm drive) in providing the runner's ability to produce optimal forward movement.

The beginning of the drive-off phase. Note the excellent symmetry between the left arm and the right leg.

Another demonstration of optimum arm and leg drive. Also note excellent angles of both feet.

Arm drive

As you use force to drive your arm back until it reaches the point at which the chest and shoulder muscles prevent it from traveling any further, the leg of the corresponding side drives forward carrying the jockey (torso) with it. Thus the motion of forward running occurs.

An effective way to think of this is in terms of firing a crossbow or bow and arrow. If the bow is drawn back in a mild, timid fashion, the flight of the arrow will be commensurate to it. On the contrary, if the bow is drawn to its fullest extent, the net result will be that the arrow will be shot with power and maximum velocity. This analogy holds true for running. If you drive your arm back in a weak fashion, then your flight time and subsequent leg drive will also be weak.

Of course, common sense has to prevail here. By optimum arm drive, I mean optimum for the distance and pace you are running. A marathoner is not going to attempt to drive her arms back with the force of a 100-meter sprinter.

The arms should remain at close to a 90-degree angle at all times. The downward arm drive of a sprinter may open up to a wider angle to provide more power with a longer lever, but for a distance runner we are looking for something more cost-efficient. Ninety degrees is the ideal angle, allowing arm levers to remain short enough to move efficiently, but long enough to help recruit the all-important *latissimus dorsi* (back muscles) to assist in generating power.

The hands should remain loose and relaxed, close to the hip bone. If the hands ride high, brushing against the side of the lower ribs, you will compromise the arm's ability to deliver the reverse thrust (à la fighter jet) necessary to assist in generating the desired pace and level of power at which you want to run.

One more point here: it is imperative that the arms do not swing across the body. You would not expect a fighter jet to be weaving its way down the runway of an aircraft carrier, so why would you run with your arms moving across your body, wasting precious energy and disrupting the smooth flow of air past your body? The less torsional rotation the better.

Up to this point in the book, all the information relating to good running biomechanics begins with your arm drive. It creates the correct amount of flight time, releases the corresponding leg to reach maximum distance, assists in propelling the torso in such a fashion as to keep you running tall and your hips up and it keeps your torso in correct posture.

FAB #3: Arm drive

Think of the arms as the pistons that turn the wheels. If the arm (piston) cadence diminishes, the legs (wheels) will slow down. Maintain a strong arm drive while keeping the shoulders relaxed and you will be able to turn a negative into a positive every time.

Mile 9.0
The Conductor and the Symphony

-

-

-

-

Over the last eight chapters, we have talked a little bit about running biomechanics. All you have to do is run tall, drive your arms, drive off your back foot, develop range of motion in your hip joints and strike optimally with the forefoot/midfoot strike. Easy, right? Well, maybe not in practice. It can be quite difficult. But nothing worthwhile in life is easy -- improved form will pay huge dividends with practice and time.

Now there is one very important topic that we have yet to discuss. All of the preceding advice is not worth the paper on which it is written without the most important ingredient of all...oxygen! After all, in order of priority, how long could we survive without food or water in comparison to O_2?

There have been many wonderful texts written on the subject of cardio-pulmonary training, offering differing opinions and facts related to methods of developing yourself as a runner, in particular, the methods used to propel yourself into peak racing shape. These texts notwithstanding, we are going to examine the subject of oxygen from a slightly different angle, since we'll be looking at how it relates to running biomechanics.

Runners come in wildly differing ages, sizes and abilities. Nevertheless there is one common golden thread that weaves its way through the tapestry of running and that thread is relaxation. Let's go through the tools we need in order to "run relaxed."

Breathing and control

Imagine for a moment, a young violinist making her debut at Carnegie Hall with the New York Philharmonic Orchestra, a violinist who will have the honor of performing a solo piece during her very first symphony.

The evening has arrived and the moment has come for her to play her piece. There are some 2,500 people in the audience and her entire family has come to witness the momentous occasion. Her adrenaline is racing, her heart is pumping seemingly out of control and her breathing is frenetic and short. She stares the conductor down as his arms wave frenetically, driving the symphony onward. In a flash, he gives her the cue she has been waiting for, and instantly she is on her feet staring out into the darkness that is her audience.

The point here is that no matter how much adrenaline our violinist is experiencing, no matter how fast her heart is beating, the symphony has its own specific rhythm and required tempo. The music must be played harmoniously and in tune. If her adrenaline gets the better of her and she plays too fast, no matter how talented a violinist she is, her music will sound grating and out of control.

For our violinist to succeed, she cannot rely on talent alone! Her talent must be combined with her experience, her hours of training and, in particular, her ability to master her adrenaline through the control of her breathing cadence. In so doing, she will fill the hall to the rafters with eloquent melodic sounds.

To achieve success in running at any level, runners too must combine their abilities with a complete awareness and control of their bodies' natural breathing cadence.

Getting out of trouble

When you run, most of the time your breathing cadence is hidden away deep in your subconscious. However, when you are conscious of your cadence, it becomes a very powerful tool to be used when attempting to get out of trouble on your run.

At speaking engagements, I am always amazed how few runners are aware of even having a cadence. Once when I was addressing several hundred runners at an expo for the Silicon Valley Marathon, I asked them the question, "How many runners here are aware of your breathing cadence when you run?" Less than a handful answered in the affirmative. This to me is somewhat akin to driving across country with no provisions or contingency plans in the event that you encounter difficulty. It is leaving everything to chance.

When I am running, most of the time I am on auto-pilot, especially on my easy days. Nevertheless, there are times, even on these easy runs, when they become a slog, this "slog" factor being magnified during fartlek training, tempo runs, hill runs, hill repeats, track workouts and races. When running, situations can arise where our breathing gets away from us. Unless we can immediately get it back under control, the prospects for the rest of that particular run or race are not good.

If, for example, you come up alongside a runner during the latter stages of a race, and you hear erratic, out-of-control breathing, chances are she is easy prey for you as you strive to move ahead of her. To the contrary, if she is breathing smoothly and running to a cadence, watch out, you have a legitimate player on your hands.

If at any time you experience difficulty during any of the above types of runs, remember to stand tall, keep your hips up, drop your shoulders, relax your belly, extend your chest and contract your mid-back muscles to open up the chest wall. Keep your head neutral, your chin tucked in and your pelvis neutral. (If you take your pelvis into anterior rotation, you will limit the hip flexors' ability to function properly, through contraction and relaxation. Doing this will limit their range of motion, which will then shorten your flight time, so negating precious extra milliseconds of relaxation. This will in turn increase the rate at which you swing your arms -- the jockey -- driving your heart rate up unnecessarily and affecting your ability to relax. This will create more negative thoughts in your head, and the whole vicious cycle will continue).

Once you have your body in the correct postural position, it is imperative to quickly regroup and reestablish your breathing rhythm. There are many cadences that can be used, which I will come to in a moment.

How to breathe

The question of "how to breathe in and out" is one that I am frequently asked at talks I give to runners all over the country. First of all, it is important to tell you that research has shown that less than 40 percent of a person's oxygen intake can be achieved via the nasal passages. When running, you must breathe in and breathe out through both nose and mouth and circulate as much air as you can. If you can breathe in and out through anywhere else, do that too!

I should add that this book is designed to address some of the scientific aspects of running with a simplistic approach, one that can be easily understood and remembered. Our cardio-pulmonary processes are extremely complex and I am certainly not qualified to try to explain the processes of gaseous exchanges that take place within the body. Nor, do I think for the purposes of this book, in its attempt to help you improve your running utilizing everyday practical advice, that it is really necessary to attempt to do so. However, if you are interested in detailed scientific information on this subject then I refer you to the Chapter entitled "Heart, Lung and Blood Dynamics during Exercise" found in Coe & Martin's *Training Distance Runners.*

Breathing cadence

When running, your body naturally falls into a certain running/breathing cadence. Often, you will find that you are striking the ground on one side or another in conjunction with the exhale phase.

As I previously suggested, on most of your runs you may not be thinking or even be conscious of such a cadence. This is fine, but it is essential to know what your natural cadence is, so that you can turn inward to it when in times of trouble.

Such times (as previously alluded to) may come during intense intervals, during a track workout, during a race, running uphill, running in extreme temperatures or wind or chasing after the last bus home.

During these times that almost all runners have or will experience, your mind might be saying something like, "I want to stop, I want to sit down, I want to quit, I want to take up a different sport, I will never do this again, or, Just let the pain stop." Sound familiar?

Well, I cannot guarantee the pain will go away, but I do have some good suggestions to help you focus, relax and to some extent take your mind off the pain and, I hope, keep you sufficiently mentally busy to help you cross the finish line in triumph.

It's time to examine the breathing cadence more closely. First, I will cover some of the available options, then I will focus on two that can easily be adopted by all runners, and more importantly, can be used with a great deal of success.

Cadence options

3 to 3 is a cadence that can be used at a slow running pace, either for a warm-up, perhaps, or for a beginning runner. Using this cadence you would take three strides while you breathe in (left, right, left, for example), and three strides while you breathe out.

3 to 2 can be used at a slightly faster pace. This can be effective during an easy paced longer run effort: faster than a warm-up but not as fast as a track workout or tempo run. Using this cadence you would take three strides while breathing in, and two while breathing out.

For a faster type tempo run or perhaps even a 10K or ten-mile race pace, you might choose a **2 to 1**. Again, this would be two strides while you breathe in, and one while you breathe out.

The two easily adoptable cadences to which I have previously referred are as follows:

3 to 1. I like this tempo as a very versatile cadence, which can be utilized all the way from warm-up to perhaps even 5K race pace for a very fit individual (at least for the first half of the race). This is where you would exhale on a certain foot strike and would then breathe in for the subsequent three strides. (i.e., OUT on right, next left, right, left all IN, then OUT on next right foot strike).

2 to 2. A common cadence, particularly at a faster pace, (half-mile race pace perhaps to a 5K pace). This cadence involves breathing in for two strides, and breathing out for two strides, very symmetrical and breathing out for two strides, very symmetrical and very rhythmic and efficient, giving you a chance for a longer exhale. It is most effective during certain longer interval track workouts or hill repeats.

Note: A **1 to 1** ratio is an option that may be used only at the end of a race in a frenetic sprint to the line from approximately 300-400 meters out. If you find yourself breathing in a one-to-one ratio, you are at the point of maximal energy expenditure. If you are in the first mile of a marathon and a person running next to you is using a 1-1 ratio, do not expect that person to be around very long in the race!

I touched on hills a moment ago, both in running hills and hill repeats (wind sprints up a hill). This requires a shorter stride pattern and an increase in stride frequency. Your breathing rate increases accordingly, depending on the pace you are running. A 2-2 cadence may be a very powerful weapon for you on those hills. Try it, and see for yourself.

Practice and experiment with cadences in your training, then once you have mastered them, tuck them away in your psychological arsenal and pull them out at opportune moments in your running and racing. Using these cadences will help you to regroup, refocus and most important of all, to be relaxed in your run. (Run Easy!)

This leads us to the last of my favorite techniques for getting out of trouble during a run...

FAB #4: Breathing

Rhythm and timing are paramount in running. When your rhythm and timing are off, running can be miserable. Early recognition of this situation followed by a swift "tune up" (a return to a rhythmic cadence with proper breathing technique) can reestablish your sense of timing, relaxation and calm. Know your breathing rhythm and use it to regain control when trouble strikes.

Mile 10.0
Joe's Story Continued...

-
-
-
-

Remember the "story of Joe" in an earlier chapter of this book? Picking up where we left off, we see that Joe is a half-mile into his 10K race (running on a dare from a friend) and currently running between half-mile and one-mile race pace. He is using all of his five feet ten inch frame, legs driving and arms pumping. He had no real finishing time goal before he started but decided early on that he could stay with his daughter's high school math teacher -- after all, his physical presence did not represent itself as much of a challenge (although he seemed to remember hearing that he fancied himself as a "bit of a runner.") This "bit of a runner" is one of the top masters runners in the area, with an all-time personal best in the 10K of 31 minutes 40 seconds some 15 years earlier and still putting in about 35 to 40 miles per week. On a good day, he can still manage to run a 35-minute 10K finishing time.

This error in judgment, magnified by that magic ingredient known as testosterone, is Joe's first mistake. His second is coming through the first mile marker in just under six minutes. Now to be fair to

Joe, running a mile in under six minutes is a very impressive feat indeed -- particularly for someone who, apart from the previous few weeks, has run sporadically at best over the prior dozen years. It certainly shows athletic ability.

However, running, as you know, is not a cheater's sport. It gives you nowhere to hide and no way to overcome the laws of both biology and physics, and just past the mile marker, the first chinks in Joe's armor begin to show.

His five-foot-ten-inch frame is now running at five-feet-eight inches. He is seemingly getting closer to the planet with every stride. Only minutes before, Joe could overcome his poor biomechanics with adrenaline and fresh legs. His heel-strike inefficiency was temporarily outweighed by an almost cartoon-like rapid rate of leg turnover. Now, however, the effects of his heel driving into the ground and having to continually lift his body up and over his front foot before being able to drive off, are beginning to take their toll on his oxygen delivery system. In other words, he is flat out beginning to tire.

First, we'll look at a little physiological detail as to what is happening at the cellular level to hasten the demise of Joe's race. There is a high accumulation of lactic acid as Joe moves beyond his lactate threshold, (the point at which lactic acid is being produced faster than it can be removed from the working muscles). It is not too long before metabolic and neuromuscular activity begins to decrease. Joe's pulmonary system is not able to deliver enough oxygen for the demands being placed upon it, and quite simply, his heart is beating too fast to be able to cope.

Now let's examine things from a biomechanical perspective. Joe's leg drive is beginning to fade by the minute. He is probably close to 100 leg strikes per minute per leg, which is way too high. Ideally, he needs to be in the high-80's to mid-90's, otherwise his stride just isn't covering enough distance, almost akin to running on the spot. Since he is not generating enough force with his drive-off, he is now creating almost no lift from his heels, and his feet are swinging through too far from his hips. Just as in the metronome analogy described earlier, the weight is a long way away from the point of axis. We know what happens now, right? The levers move at a slower and less efficient rate, and Joe is going nowhere fast.

Joe's midsection (i.e., his abdominal and lower back muscles), not adapted to the stresses of running, start to collapse inwardly, as do his shoulders as he begins to round forward. Now he is fighting gravity in a very inefficient manner, as his skeletal muscles are no longer aligned atop each other. To add insult to injury, since his shoulders are hunched over, he is now contracting his chest muscles, applying undue pressure on his rib-cage. This fact, along with his head being pressed too far down, as he is not strong enough to support it properly (the jockey is falling off the front of the horse,) compounds his biggest problem of all -- his inability to get enough air. He is struggling to breathe, and the "violinist" is completely out of synch with the symphony.

The final link in this sad chain of events, the one that really finishes him off from a biomechanical perspective, is that his arm drive is now weak at best. The same arm drive that just eight minutes before was so decisive, so crisp and so bold, has now fizzled to a feeble gesture that barely extends behind his torso. His arms are now somewhere up around his mid-rib area, with hardly any counter rotational force being generated (that "crossbow" hardly being drawn at all). With his corresponding leg, there is no drive, no lift, no flight, and ultimately no Joe in the race. He is beaten by ego initially, and along with his poor cardiopulmonary conditioning, his ultimate defeat comes from very poor biomechanics. Joe's day in this race is over! Against his name in the finishing results, those infamous letters: Joe...DNF (Did Not Finish).

Contributing to the richness of our sport is the fact that there is nowhere to hide. Running exposes all those who dare to take shortcuts. Next time you are at a local running race, whether you are competing or cheering on, look out for Joe. He will be there; he always is. Long live Joe, as he serves as a very keen reminder of the way not to do things when it comes to the sport of running, or come to think of it, anything else in life.

Mile 11.0
Performance Strength-Training
Specific to Running

•

•

•

•

As a professional running coach, I firmly believe that
in order to improve as a runner, you need to run on a
consistent basis. Furthermore, in order to become a
faster runner, you need, at the appropriate times, to
run fast. What I am saying here is that running is a
sport that places very specific demands on the body
and in order to achieve maximum adaptation of its
neurological, musculoskeletal and cardio-pulmonary
systems, there is simply no substitute for running
itself.

That said, I am also a firm believer in strength-training
as a key method of improving your running. A proper
strength-training regimen can give your body the
foundation and framework necessary to reduce your
workout and race recovery times. It can also provide
the platform you need to be able train and race more
competitively.

In essence, the main object of strength-training
(sometimes referred to as resistance training) is to
break down a particular muscle or muscle group.

Such a break-down forces the body to regenerate itself to a higher degree of strength than has been previously experienced. (We discuss the methods for this in more detail later in this chapter). While it may be controversial to say that you can strength-train in a manner specifically designed to replicate running, I firmly believe that, when employed correctly, certain methods of strength-training align themselves more closely than others to the biomechanics of running. Increased functional strength provides increased esteem and confidence, and confidence in our running ability plays a major part in a sport that is very psychological as well as physical.

Specific strength-training

Specific strength-training using good technique over a sustained period of time can directly help runners achieve good biomechanics.

Let's examine this more closely. A gifted runner may have been blessed with good mechanics, good posture, proper arm drive, correct carriage position, etc. therein having the ability to move her body forward in a very efficient manner. Consistent training might also have provided her with good lower body strength. However, running itself does not guarantee strength and stability through the core area, (specifically the lower back, mid-back, abdominal and abductor/adductor muscles -- basically the inner and outer thigh and hip muscles). In the latter stages of a long run or intense workout or race, any weakness in her core area will compromise her muscle integrity and "gifted mechanics" will give way to poor posture and a breakdown in form. This will increase her potential for injury, and in a race context might mean the difference between victory and defeat.

This problem is not limited to the core area. We have already discussed the importance of the arm drive. Mechanically, nothing positive happens until that arm is driven back providing the counter-force to certain reactions that then result in forward locomotion. If the arm drive becomes impaired, the "flight time" is compromised and again, things ultimately fall apart. Strengthening the "shoulder girdle" (shoulders, chest, neck and upper back muscles) along with the arms can prevent this premature fatigue, once again providing the potential for optimal biomechanics over a sustained period of time.

These days it is easy to find books on strength-training that will prepare you for a multitude of sports. Additionally, there are activities such as Pilates, a method of training that has been around for almost a century, and various styles of Yoga, a method of strength-training and meditation that has been around much longer than that. These two focus on core stabilization and correct methods of breathing, both of which are integral to improved running biomechanics. Indeed, there are so many options when embarking on a new strength-training regimen, knowing where to start can be quite the daunting task. From my point of view though I understand that the majority of runners lead very busy lives and have a multitude of daily commitments, not the least of which is running itself. With this in mind I have selected my top 20 strength-training exercises, each exercise being specifically designed to help you increase your overall strength *as a runner*.

Equipment and equipment alternatives

Before we get started, let's look at some of the
equipment you may decide to use as an aid to your
strength-training. As you have been reading this
chapter, you may have been thinking that before
getting your strength-training underway you would
have to shell out some money and join a gym. There
are a couple of good reasons why this is not the case.
When starting out in a gym it is easy to find yourself
feeling overwhelmed and intimidated by the wide
range and apparent complexity of strength-training
apparatus on hand. Some of the machines give the
impression that you need a license to operate them.
Even with several years' experience working in and
around a health club setting, I can still be confused by
the machinery. Sometimes I find myself looking at a
machine and thinking, "It looks good, but what on
earth is it for?" Or more accurately, "Which muscle
group does it train?" Well, there is no need to be
intimidated -- I can tell you from experience that while
some of this equipment is very good, much of it is
superfluous.

Moving on to the second reason why it may not be
necessary or possible for you to join a gym: as with
any good workout program, your strength-training
schedule has to fit it into your regular schedule. It
may well be that you simply do not have the time to
come home from work, get changed, look at that comfy
couch, resist it, return an email or phone call or two,
get back in the car and drive to the club, find
somewhere to park, check in, go to the locker room to
take off your sweats and finally get into the gym. And
if you have kids -- well, you can pretty much forget it!
Of course, I am not suggesting that this is the case for

everyone: I am just making light of a point that for many of you may have hit close to home -- it can be quite a hassle to go through this kind of drill on a regular basis. Nor am I implying that you should not join a health club; far from it, they offer an invaluable service. If you have the time, or make the time, to get to the health club before or after work or on the weekends or both, then that is terrific. I just know from firsthand experience coaching in the "trenches" that for large sections of the population, this just is not a realistic option.

While we're on the subject, I've heard just about all of the alternatives out there for the busy athlete. Most of them are also completely unrealistic. Yes, I know you can probably squeeze in 300 seated crunches in your car while driving to work and back, but is this really practical and is it really safe? Yes, you can probably drop down to the floor at the office in between phone calls and do ten pushups, but again, I ask you, how long will you keep that up? A day?

In summary, the following strength-training information is equally applicable regardless of your experience in strength-training and whether you prefer to train in a health club setting or in the privacy of your own home.

Recommended equipment:

The following pieces of equipment should all be easy to find at quality retail sporting good stores.

Medicine ball

The medicine ball is an extremely versatile and space-efficient piece of equipment, one that is useful for many different exercises. For example, it can be used to add resistance when doing squats and to provide an unstable platform for the experienced athlete when doing push-ups. These push-ups are performed with the hands on the ball, forcing the core area to stabilize the body during both the lifting and the lowering phase. The medicine ball can also be used to add resistance to crunches.

Medicine balls come in varying weights and sizes and range in price from around $15 to $50 depending on the weight. Weights generally range from 2lbs up to about 15lbs.

Coach GP's recommendation:
Purchase a 4-6lb ball (novice) 8lb - 12lb (experienced)

Stability (or exercise) ball

Stability balls have become very popular in recent years. They can be found in health clubs, rehabilitation centers, personal training studios, high schools, colleges and even in offices and homes. They are relatively inexpensive and they provide a supportive, safe but intentionally unstable base, forcing you to challenge and strengthen your coordination, balance and stability by working all of your smaller muscles as well as your larger, stronger muscles. If you are unfamiliar with this particular type of ball, it resembles a good old fashioned beach ball.

Some examples of possible "on the ball" exercises include pushups, dips, hip raises, crunches, seated shoulder press, chest press, lat pullover, hamstring curls and many more.

Approximate cost is $15 to $30. Benefits: They challenge stability and balance; they are space-efficient and very mobile as they can be deflated and inflated as required.

Coach GP's recommendation: If you are 5'8" or shorter then purchase a ball that is 45cm-55cm. If you are taller than 5'8" then purchase a ball that is 65cm-75cm.

Dumbbells

Dumbbells are space-efficient, cost-effective and versatile, and they can be used for a great many upper body exercises. They allow for unilateral exercise, meaning they allow you to work one side of your body at a time preventing the dominant side from performing most of the work.

Most retailers sell dumbbells by the pound. They are now available with protective coatings to make them more user-friendly and less destructive to have in your home.

Although you can spend a great deal less by purchasing piecemeal, you can purchase an all-inclusive set for less than $200.

Coach GP's recommendation: In most cases for runners, weights from 5lbs up to 50lbs are all you need.

Resistance bands

In essence, resistance bands are rubberized bands that provide uniform resistance in both their contraction phase and their expansion phase. Also known as resistance tubes, they have been used by therapists and sports medicine doctors for over 20 years and are now very much a part of the home and health club workout. Extremely versatile and space-efficient, they can be used for both lower and upper body exercises. They are excellent for rehabilitation work such as rotator cuff or hip-strengthening.

Resistance bands typically cost $10 or less depending on their length.

Workout bench

A workout bench is a helpful aid to have for home use, enabling you to perform a variety of exercises. They are generally priced at $50 - $200.

Stretching rope (8' long)

There are various stretching methods available to the athlete, static stretching or PNF (proprioceptive neuromuscular facilitation) stretching, to name but two. My preferred method of stretching is "Active Isolated (A.I.) Stretching." I believe it is both the most gentle and effective method of promoting increased range of motion and flexibility. It also serves as a great warmup for the muscles.

A.I. stretching works on a two-second stretching principle whereby you actively contract the opposing muscle to the target muscle that you are stretching. For example, if you want to stretch your hamstring muscles, you need to actively contract your quadriceps muscles. It is easy to learn, and the only equipment recommended is an eight-foot rope or cord for self-assistance.

Two of the foremost authorities on this type of stretching are the father and son team of Jim and Phil Wharton. They are the authors of several books including *The Whartons' Stretch Book* which is simply excellent, a must have in every runner's library. It is the most complete and most relevant stretch book of its kind and I have recommended it to many of my athletes with great success. *The Whartons' Stretch Book* is available at www.whartonperformance.com.

Alternatives in a pinch!

For the budget-conscious athlete, or if you don't happen to have your equipment handy, dumbbells can be replaced with either soup cans or telephone books. You could use either item for many of the exercises that follow in Chapters 13 through 15.

Strength-training language

Now let's go over some terminologies that crop up in and around the weight room.

Reps:
Repetitions of an exercise within a set.
Example: A singular contraction and release of a muscle or group of muscles against a specific resistance = 1 repetition.

Sets:
A number of repetitions of a particular exercise.
Example 10 repetitions = 1 set.

Muscular Endurance:
The ability of muscles to sustain work over time.

Muscular Strength:
Maximal amount of force delivered or produced via a single muscular contraction.

Adaptive training:

Adaptive training takes advantage of one of the basic scientific principles of exercise -- the fact that muscles subjected to stress will adapt to a level at which they can handle that stress. In other words, when training is performed properly, there is stress to the muscle groups. During recovery there will be an adaptive process that occurs as a result of this stress, this is known as *the training effect*. In order to keep this training effect going, there must be progression. To maintain this progression when strength-training, you must first start out using an appropriate weight for a particular exercise. Then, over a series of workouts, you must increase the number of repetitions you perform. At a point when you can comfortably achieve 12-15 repetitions, you can probably move up to the next level of weight but don't forget to return to a lower starting number of repetitions for that exercise.

Warm-up

I'm sure you would not consider running a hard track workout without having jogged several warm-up laps beforehand. Preparation for your strength-training is of equal importance.

The warm-up serves to raise the core body temperature to adequate levels, increase the suppleness in the muscles and soft tissue, prepare your central nervous system and heighten your psychological awareness and your proprioception.**

There is no need for anything complex; just 5-10 minutes of gentle cardiovascular exercise such as bike-riding or jogging will suffice. Just remember that prior to any workout it is critical to bring your body into a physiological state that sufficiently prepares it for the task at hand.

** *The unconscious perception of movement and spatial orientation arising from stimuli within the body itself.*

Caution:

Finally -- be sure to use your common sense -- if you suffer from any serious medical problems, such as heart disease, diabetes or high blood pressure, or if you are over 40, please see your doctor before beginning any strength-training regimen.

Breathing and control

Be sure to utilize good breathing when strength-training, ideally exhaling whenever you lift against gravity. Most importantly, just breathe, do not hold your breath. Use slow controlled movements.

What to do:

Over the course of the next three chapters, I will be taking you through my top 20 exercises. These exercises will help all runners strength-train in a safe, effective and time-efficient manner. They require little or no investment in equipment and most can be safely performed at home.

Strength-training should cover all the major muscle groups: chest, shoulders, back, arms, abdominal muscles and legs. My strength-training exercises are separated into the following three groups:

1   **Core Stabilization**

2   **Upper Body**

3   **Lower Body**

One important note from the perspective of running biomechanics is that while I strongly advocate a regular Active Isolated Stretching regimen be included in your training (as previously mentioned) it is not essential for the runner to have ballerina-like soft tissue flexibility. It is, however, extremely important to have excellent range of motion within the articulated joints, specifically, the ankles, knees, hips and shoulders.

I will note below which exercises are safe for all levels immediately, and which should only be attempted after 30 or 90 days by newcomers to strength-training. After a brief explanation of core strength and stability, we will get right to my recommended exercises in Mile 13.

Mile 12.0
It's in the Core, That's Where It's At!

•

•

•

•

Core stabilization. What does it mean?

If you look at an anatomical muscle chart that shows a cross-section of the major muscle groups in the human body, you may notice that "all roads lead to central" -- my way of saying that all of the major muscle groups, i.e., the upper leg, back, gluteus and abdominal muscles, all lead to the body's center of gravity. This provides a central region for strength and stability.

My definition of core stability is "the ability of our muscular/neural system to give maximum support to our skeletal system in its fight against gravity."

One of the key elements to strengthening our core is in the strengthening of the muscles that follow the channel of the spine (i.e., the spinal erectors and mid/upper back muscles).

Take for example the hammer and discus throwers that we might be lucky enough to witness during the Olympic Games. Think about watching these athletes enter the throwing area, their set-up position and specifically, the way they coil their bodies prior to beginning their throws. It is in these coils that the athletes' muscular forces are first harnessed and then swiftly released, producing spectacularly explosive results.

In effect, what these athletes are doing is creating a "separation" between their shoulders and their hips, an east-west, north-south relationship between the body's upper and lower joints. Try standing up and facing a mirror with your hips and shoulders parallel to each other. Next, while your hips remain still, slowly rotate your shoulders in a clockwise direction until they are perpendicular (or 90 degrees) to your hips. You have now created a shoulder-hip "separation," which happens to be a very powerful way to create torsion in your spinal muscles. When uncoiled with velocity, this torsion can generate tremendous force.

What's the point?

The following core stabilization exercises incorporate this principle of shoulder/hip separation in order to create torsional power and increase your body's core strength. Consider this: running requires torso rotation with every stride. If, as you can clearly see by watching many runners run, this torso rotation is left unmanaged, your running direction will remain rudderless and weak. You will also succumb to fatigue much sooner than necessary. On the other hand, if you improve your ability to control and manage your torsional rotation, you will improve your body's ability to withstand the impact forces of running and provide a stronger platform from which to generate greater flight time. Flight time, as I'm sure you remember, is the second of the two key components essential to proper running biomechanics.

During all core exercises, you should concentrate on lengthening your body and remaining tall relative to your own height. When strength-training in either a seated or a standing position, always keep yourself "in extension," that is to say, with chest up, shoulders back (not rounded forward) and with a slight anterior (forward) rotation to your pelvis. This will help you to remain in a strong stable position and protect your lower back.

Once again, if you have never attempted strength-training, or have any preexisting back or other conditions, please consult with your physician before undertaking these exercises.

Mile 13.0
The Runner's Power. My Top 20!

•

•

•

Note: "All levels" indicates that a particular exercise can be performed by all athletes right from the beginning of their program. "30 or 90 days" indicates the recommended number of days a novice athlete should wait before performing that exercise.

Exercises for the Jockey

Hip flexors/Oblique abdominal muscles/Spinal erectors

Russian Twist
(Basic exercise, all levels)

Sit upright, legs in V

Lean slightly back, contracting abdominal muscles

Hold ball, arms out in front head level and facing forward

Rotate arms from hip to hip

Sit in an upright position, legs out in front of the body, position legs in a "V" formation. Lean back slightly, contract the abdominal muscles. Take a medicine ball, extend the arms so the ball is held out in front of the body. Head is level, facing forward.

Beginning with the ball out in front of the face, rotate the arms down to hip level on one side. Next, rotate the arms back to the starting position. Repeat the whole movement to the other side. Be sure to keep the hips "facing" forward throughout.

As you turn, the shoulders will rotate; their finishing position will be at 90 degrees to the hips. The outside arm will remain fairly straight through the movement and the inside arm will bend as it turns.

■■■■■■■■■■

Single Leg "V" Ups
(Basic exercise, all levels)

Improves range of motion in hip and shoulder joints

Lie supine (on the back), arms extended straight overhead. Keep the pelvis neutral and the back flat. Bring one straight arm/hand over the chest to meet with its opposing leg/foot,

Lie supine

Arms overhead

Raise one arm toward opposite leg

Lower to starting position slowly and under control

Repeat with opposite arm and leg

now lower both arm and leg to the ground. Maintain control throughout each movement. Maintain the integrity of your back on the floor. Repeat the exercise alternating opposite quadrants as you go.

■ ■ ■ ■ ■ ■ ■ ■ ■ ■

Single Leg V Ups
(Advanced exercise, 90 days)

Abdominal/Hip/Low-back/Shoulder muscles/Improves range of motion in hip and shoulder joints

Lie supine, arms extended straight overhead. Keep the pelvis neutral and the back flat. Raise both arms and feet four to six inches off the ground -- this is the starting position.

Lie supine, arms overhead

Maintain arms, head and legs 4 - 6 inches off the ground

Keep back flat and abdominals contracted

Raise one arm toward opposite leg

Repeat with opposite arm and leg

Bring one straight arm/hand over the chest to meet with its opposing leg/foot, then lower both arm and leg to the starting position. Contract the abdominals. Breathe evenly. Do not allow the arms, hands, legs or feet to touch the ground at any time. Maintain control throughout each movement. Maintain the integrity of the back on the floor. Repeat the exercise alternating opposite quadrants as you go.

■■■■■■■■■■

Double Leg V Ups
(Advanced exercise, 90 days)

Abdominal/Hip/Low-back/Shoulder muscles/
Improves range of motion in hip and shoulder joints.

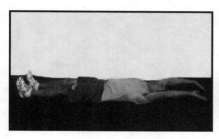

Lie supine

Arms extended overhead

Perform a crunch raising hands toward feet

Feet remain off the ground throughout the movement

Assume the same starting position as for the previous exercise. Next, simultaneously raise both the legs and the arms, moving each toward the other. The arms/ hands are aspiring toward the toes.

Slowly return to the starting position without fully releasing the shoulder blades to the floor. This ensures that the abdominal muscles remain contracted throughout the entire set.

As with the two previous exercises, be sure to maintain control throughout each movement.

■■■■■■■■■■

Eagles
(Basic exercise, all levels)

Strengthens hips flexors/Improves range of motion in the hip joints

Lie supine with the back flat, arms extended out to sides. Arms should be in line with the shoulders, palms down. Taking one leg at a time, lift and move the leg in a slow controlled swing across the body.

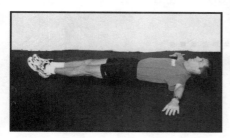

Lie supine with back flat. Have arms extended out to the side, in line with the shoulders, palms down.

Lifting one leg at a time, take a slow, controlled swing across the body.

Touch the foot down on the ground, positioned at right angles to the torso.

Touch the foot down at 90 degrees to the torso. Now return the leg back to the starting position. Repeat to the other side.

While performing this exercise, keep the back of the shoulders and arms pressed into the ground, maintaining a stretch in the shoulder joints. Begin with a modest foot placement, then as you warm up, try to walk the foot up toward the hands. Notice that at the point when the foot touches down, you will once again have created a shoulder/hip separation.

∎ ∎ ∎ ∎ ∎ ∎ ∎ ∎ ∎ ∎

Reverse Eagles
(Basic exercise, all levels)

Hips extensors/Low-back/Improves range of motion in the hip joints

Lie prone

Arms at right angles to torso

Lie prone (face down) arms extended out to sides. Arms should be in line with your shoulders, palms down. Head is face down.

Alternate leg sweeps toward opposite hand

Return to start position

Bending at the knee, swing one leg over and across the body, creating a stretch in the hip flexor. Touch the toe to the ground. Return leg to starting position and repeat other side. Once again this will create shoulder/hip separation.

Note: As you work through this exercise it is not necessary to try to reach the hands with the toes.

Back Extensions with Dips to the Side
(Basic exercise, 30 days)

Abdominals and obliques/Low-back/Mid-back/Gluteus/Improves range of motion in the back and shoulder joints

Lie prone, arms behind head
Contract gluteus

Raise torso to "up" position

Rotate elbow down

Return to "up" position

Lower, raise and rotate to other side

Lie prone, hands placed behind the head. Hips, legs and feet remain on the ground. Contract your gluteus muscles for support. Now lift up/extend through your mid/upper back, raising your torso off the ground (or stability ball as shown here) to a comfortable degree. Next, while in the "up" position, rotate or dip one elbow down toward the ground. (Be sure to contract the gluteus muscles before raising the torso -- this provides important strength and assistance to the muscles of the mid and upper back. Also maintain a contraction of your shoulder blades through the entire set -- in effect stretching out your chest).

After the dip, return to the "up" position, lower to the starting position, then raise back up again and rotate/ dip the other elbow to the ground. Return to the "up" position and lower your torso to the starting position. Use good breathing; raise and lower with control. The neck should be in alignment with the spinal cord at all times. Repeat the sequence.

This exercise will most likely require some practice before you find a comfortable breathing pattern.

▪▪▪▪▪▪▪▪▪▪

Crunches
(All levels)

Superior region of abdominals.

Lie supine, hands behind head to support neck

Crunch up a few inches exhaling as you lift

Return to start position; repeat

When it comes to crunches, a very effective method of increasing their challenge and maximizing their benefit is to use an unstable platform such as a stabilization ball. Doing so requires all the abdominal, lower back and hip muscles to assist in the work.

Beginning with the more familiar "floor" method: lie supine with the knees bent and the feet planted on the floor. Place the hands behind the head. Shoulder blades should be contracted (chest stretched). Support the head. Keep the head and neck in alignment with the spine at all times. Contract the abdominal muscles by "crunching" up several inches, no more. Exhale while lowering back to the starting position.

<u>On the ball</u>

The following instructions are for performing the crunch on the highly recommended stability ball.

Lie supine over the ball, so that the ball provides plenty of support for your low back and torso. The feet should be planted on the floor. Place the hands behind the head with shoulder blades contracted (chest stretched). Support the head. Keep the head and neck in alignment with the spine at all times. Contract the abdominal muscles by "crunching" up several inches, no more. Exhale while lowering back to the starting position. For a more advanced exercise, lift one leg off the floor. Hold the (straight) leg out in front of the body. Find a stable position on the ball, then perform the crunch as before. Maintain the contraction in the abdominal cavity throughout the entire movement.

■ ■ ■ ■ ■ ■ ■ ■ ■ ■

Oblique Crunches
(All levels)

Oblique region of abdominals.

As in previous exercise except:

Rotate elbow towards opposite knee as you lift

Return to starting position, repeat other side

This exercise is basically the same as the previous one, but this time the shoulders and elbows are rotated during the "crunch" phase. This rotation creates a more precise contraction of the oblique abdominal muscles (the abs located at the side of the lower torso). These muscles are largely responsible for maintaining the integrity of the core region. During the lowering phase the shoulders and elbows are rotated back to the starting position. Repeat the exercise. Alternate sides through each set.

■ ■ ■ ■ ■ ■ ■ ■ ■ ■

Reverse Crunches
(All levels)

Inferior region of abdominals.

Lie supine, hands behind head (novice) or hands face down to side of hips (advanced)

Raise knees over hips

Tilt pelvis, knees towards chest

Lower to start position. Repeat

Lie supine. Lift the knees directly over the hips. The lower legs remain parallel to the floor making a 90-degree angle to the upper legs. Place hands by the sides (advanced) or under the tail bone (novice). Using as little support as possible from the hands, pull the knees backward in the direction of the head. Keep inching back until you feel a good contraction of the lower (inferior) region of the abdominal muscles. Note, this will require only a small movement.

Now for the lowering phase, inhale and slowly return the legs to the point where your knees are directly over the hips. Use control. Do not let the full weight of the hips and pelvis touch the floor. The correct way to perform this exercise is to begin the next repetition before reaching the point at which all the tension is released from the abdominal cavity.

As shown in the photographs, this exercise can also be performed on a bench, in which case the hands should be overhead and gripping the top edge (good for all levels).

■ ■ ■ ■ ■ ■ ■ ■ ■ ■

Mile 14.0
Upper Body Strength-Training (Trunk)
"The Jockey"

-
-
-

As you work your way through the following upper body exercises, try to concentrate on maintaining good biomechanics and excellent posture. Be aware of the position of the body in relation to its surroundings. Maintain good head position and good fluid breathing throughout. Make sure you keep the back in the correct position at all times. This is especially important when an exercise requires that you keep the back flat against the bench or exercise ball. When working at the freestyle exercises (those that don't require the use of a machine or bench) be sure to keep the shoulder blades retracted in what is known as "extension". This will prevent the shoulders from rounding and, most importantly, will insure that the body remains in a strong stable position throughout each exercise.

∎ ∎ ∎ ∎ ∎ ∎ ∎ ∎ ∎ ∎

Pull-ups
(All levels)

Back/Chest/Shoulders/Arms

Place hands on pull up bar, palms up

Raise torso until chin is level with the bar

Engage back muscles and exhale as you lift

Lower with control

This is an extremely hard exercise for most people, but it is a very effective method of strengthening the body to an extent where it can efficiently handle the dynamic movement of its own weight. Pull-ups are performed almost exclusively in a gym setting, however it is possible to purchase and install a horizontal pull-up bar. If you do install the bar, please be certain both that it is secure and that it is strong enough to support several times your body weight.

If you are already familiar with the exercise, I recommend completing two sets at close to maximum effort, allowing for adequate but minimum recovery between sets and utilizing two different hand grips. *First grip*: Hands shoulder-width apart, palms up. Place hands on the bar. Exhale and raise torso until chin is level with the bar. Engage the back muscles as you lift. Lower the body with control. *Second grip:* Known as a chinup. Use a narrower grip, palms facing in. Perform exercise as before.

The combination of the two different grips will maximize the benefit to the arms, chest and back muscles. Make sure to lower with control and always complete the full range of motion.

Place hands on pull up bar, narrow grip, palms facing in

Raise torso until chin is level with the bar

Engage back muscles and exhale as you lift

Lower with control

Note for novices: Your goal should be to complete one pull-up. If you find this is not yet possible, begin by performing a negative pull-up. Stand on a box that allows you to reach and hold onto the pull-up bar. Use a narrow grip, chinup style. Step off the box. Maintain the position for a second at the apex of the pull-up. Then inhale and lower the body with control; keep lowering until the feet touch the ground. (If necessary perform this negative pull-up with the assistance of a partner. The partner should provide support by holding onto your hips).

Step back up on the box and repeat five to six times if possible. Over the course of 30 days, if performed two to three times per week, you should develop sufficient strength to attempt a full pull-up. If you are still unable to complete one after 30 days, continue with negative pull-ups by increasing the repetitions each week, periodically challenging yourself to do a regular pull-up. Persist and you will succeed. Always make sure to breathe through the entire movement.

■ ■ ■ ■ ■ ■ ■ ■ ■ ■

Pushups - The Old Classic!
(All levels except beginner)

Chest/Back/Arms/Shoulders/Core Stability

This is an exercise that gives us all the chills. Why is that? Over the years I have performed thousands of pushups but whenever I give them to my athletes I am always treated to the same response "Oh no, not pushups!"

Yup, pushups...the old staple...one of the premier exercises for strengthening the chest, back and arms. It requires core stabilization in order to perform each repetition.

Keep torso straight, hands shoulder width apart, exhale as you lift, lower with control

For regular pushups: Keep torso straight, hands shoulder-width apart, abdominal muscles contracted. Lowering phase -- arms hinge at the elbow, the elbows remain close to the torso and do not stray outward. Lower with control. Upper arm should finish at 90 degrees to the lower arm. The torso and head should finish just above the ground. Pushup phase -- exhale as you lift.

An innovative, more advanced way to do pushups is for the athlete to place the feet on a large stability (or beach type) ball. As shown in the photographs, place the hands on the ground, shoulder-width apart and complete pushups with a full range of motion (as in regular pushups). The inclusion of this type of unstable surface forces the core muscles to work extra hard just to keep the body in a neutral starting position.

Advanced pushups -- feet on exercise or beach ball

 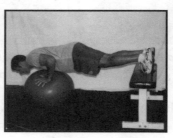

Very advanced pushups --feet on bench, hands on exercise or beach ball

For very advanced athletes, try performing pushups with the feet on a bench and the hands placed close together on a ball. You will feel an extra intensity, particularly in your triceps and forearms.

Beginner pushups
(No knees down)

For those of you thinking about doing a pushup with your knees on the floor, don't waste your time. Here is the plan for you. Just as you perform "negative" pull-ups, so you can perform negative pushups. They will certainly take some extra effort on your part, but it will be well worth it.

Starting position -- begin on all fours, the hands shoulder-width apart and the feet slightly closer together. Raise the hips until only the hands and feet remain on the ground. Now for the hard part -- walk the hands forward until your body is straight and knees, hips and shoulders are in line. Next, inhale and slowly lower the body to the floor. Focus on lowering with control. Take as much time as is possible to complete the whole movement -- up to five seconds if you can. Once on the floor, rest a moment or two, return to the all fours position and repeat the movement. Complete as many as you can -- increasing the repetitions until you can comfortably complete two sets of ten. (Take a 60-second break or as long as you need to remain comfortable between each set). Once you can complete two sets of ten repetitions, you are ready to begin regular pushups (see previous exercise). Congratulations!

■ ■ ■ ■ ■ ■ ■ ■ ■ ■

One Arm Row
(All levels)

Back/ Arms/ Shoulders

Keep back flat, neck in line with spine. Raise weight under control. Bring weight alongside hip.

This exercise can be done with the help of a bench or stability ball. Alternatively you can simply lean the torso forward, using the front leg for support.

If using a bench and strengthening the left side -- begin by selecting an appropriate weight. Place the right knee and also the right hand on the bench. Left leg should be straight, the left foot placed on the ground about one shoulder-width away from the body and slightly behind the hip. The back should be flat, not rounded or hunched, the neck should be in alignment with your spine. Inhale to begin, then, on the exhale, start to lift the weight with the left arm. Raise slowly, under control and in a slight backward motion (as if you were sawing a piece of wood). Bring the weight alongside the hip and then return it to the starting position. Complete two sets of 10-12 repetitions, then switch sides, or alternatively complete one set per side and repeat.

If you are not using a bench or ball for support, complete the exercise in almost the same fashion, but place the right leg out in front of the body. The right leg should be slightly bent. Place the right hand on the thigh, just above the knee (not on the kneecap) and lean forward. Be sure to maintain a straight back alignment. Complete the exercise as described above.

■ ■ ■ ■ ■ ■ ■ ■ ■ ■

Incline Chest Press
(All levels)

Shoulders/Chest/Arms

This exercise is my secret weapon! Let's do it...

Use a 45° incline bench

Hands out to sides, level with shoulders, forearms at 90° to upper arms

Press dumbbells upward, maintaining shoulder-width distance between hands, exhale as you lift

Return to start and repeat

Set up an incline bench at about a 45-degree angle and select your weights. This exercise relies almost exclusively on a small muscle group in the shoulders with the dumbbells being held away from the body. For these two reasons you will find that you are better off beginning with a fairly light weight.

Sit on the incline bench with the lumbar spine (lower back area) pressed firmly into the seat-back. Hold a dumbbell in each hand, bring the hands up to shoulder level. The upper and lower arms should form a 90-degree angle. Keep the hands out wide, just outside the line of the shoulder. To help determine if you are in the correct position, trace an imaginary line from hand to hand across your chest. The arms should be in "football goal post" position.

Now -- with authority -- press the dumbbells away from the body until your arms are out straight. The hands should remain shoulder-width apart. Return to the starting position. Repeat 10-12 times, completing one to two sets. Do not increase the weight until two sets seem comfortable. Also note, depending on your neck "design" you might feel more comfortable with your head pressed back into the top of the incline bench, or you might feel better with the head lifted slightly away from the bench. I have tried both positions and providing you are using the appropriate weight, both are fine.

It is very important to keep your lower back pressed into the bench and your abdominal muscles contracted throughout the entire movement and to exhale as you press out.

Adaptation for the exercise ball. Begin by lying back on the ball with the feet placed in front of you, feet should be wide enough apart to provide a stable platform. Slide the body down the ball toward the floor so that the ball fits snugly against your back and shoulder. The torso should be leaning back against the ball in an incline position. (Note: Place your weights on the floor close to the ball before you begin so that they are easy to pick up once you are in position). Complete the exercise as described for the incline bench.

This exercise develops both front and outside shoulder strength -- strength upon which you'll be able to rely whether you are using it in a final kick against the clock or against an opponent in an upcoming race!

▪ ▪ ▪ ▪ ▪ ▪ ▪ ▪ ▪ ▪

Lat Pullover
(All levels)

Chest/Back/Mid Back/Arms/Shoulders/Range of Motion in Shoulder Joints

This is an excellent strength and range of motion exercise for the above-listed muscle groups.

Lie supine, hold weight over chest

Inhale, lower weight behind head
Return to start, exhale as you lift

Lie back on the stability ball placing the feet shoulder-width apart and flat on the floor. It is extremely important that the hips are pressed upward while the abdominal muscles are contracted -- maintaining the integrity and strength of the body from the knees through to the shoulders. Both neck and head must be supported by the ball and remain in alignment with the rest of the body.

Adaptation for the bench. Lie back on the bench. Feet are either on the end of the bench, with legs bent and feet flat, or straddling the bench so the feet are on the floor. It is imperative that the lumbar spine remains firmly pressed against the bench.

Now that you are set -- take a single dumbbell and hold it in a vertical position by cupping the hands under and around the weight's top end. The weight should hang straight down, perpendicular to the ground. In this exercise the weight should both start and finish in a position directly over the sternum (breastbone). To begin, take the hands back over the head, keeping the arms straight. When you reach the point at which the shoulders will not travel any further, bend slightly at the elbow to squeeze out a little extra range of motion. Do not force the issue -- as your body becomes more familiar with the exercise, the range of motion will slightly increase. This in turn will help the arm's range of motion when you are running (remember the fighter jet, crossbow and swimming pool?) Finally, straighten the arms so that the forearms align with the upper arms, then return the straightened arms to the starting position over the sternum.

Inhale deeply during the lowering phase; this will help to expand the chest cavity. Exhale as you lift. (When it comes to running, practicing deep breathing is an excellent exercise in its own right).

The Lat Pullover will strengthen the "wings on your back" (i.e., *the latissimus dorsi*) as well as the chest and arm muscles. As previously mentioned, this will increase upper body power and improve your running.

■ ■ ■ ■ ■ ■ ■ ■ ■ ■

Dips/Bench Dips
(All levels)

Chest/Back/Arms/Shoulders.

If you are strength-training in a gym, then take advantage of the dip bar for this exercise (ask the personal trainer on duty to point it out if necessary). Training at home? Don't worry, there are other equipment alternatives available for dips, we'll discuss them in moment.

For the advanced athlete: First note that the head should be kept level and the shoulder blades kept retracted throughout. This will ensure that you are once again "in extension" and not rounded in the back (see end of Mile 12).

Stand on the dip bar supports and place each hand on the parallel bars by your sides, palms-down. Step off the leg supports and either bend your lower legs up behind you at a 90-degree angle to the upper legs, or cross them over. While maintaining complete control of the body (not letting it swing), bend the arms and lower slowly to a position where the upper arm and shoulder are slightly higher than your elbow (not lower!) Return to the starting position by driving upwards using the strength of the arms, the arms should reach an extended or straightened position. Do not touch the feet down until the last repetition is complete.

For athletes new to strength-training: Sit on the edge of a bench or exercise ball. Place the hands next to the hips, fingers should either be curled over the edge of the bench or resting on top of the ball, facing forward. Feet should be in a firm shoulder-width stance.

Slide the buttocks just off the edge of the bench or ball. Bend the arms and lower the torso as described for the advanced exercise, only in this version the feet will provide support. Lower the body to a point where the shoulder is just above the height of the elbow (not below) and return to the starting position.

Hands behind you on bench or ball. Lower until the angle between upper and lower arms is approaching 90 degrees. Return to start, exhale as you lift.

If you are completely new to the exercise: If you are just starting out, then try to complete just one repetition at a time with a short recovery in between. Be consistent with this exercise until you can build up to two sets of 25 repetitions.

Once this goal has been attained this would be the time to graduate to the dip bar. Begin with fewer repetitions and work your way up from there. If you are strength-training at home, then continue to use the bench or the ball and just keep increasing your repetitions by adding more sets.

If you happen to be using a bench, there is another method by which you can increase the degree of difficulty. Simply place your feet, with legs straight out in front of you, onto another bench or chair. The intensity of the exercise will now approach that of regular "dip bar" dips.

Mile 15.0 Lower Body Strength-Training "The Race Horse"

-
-
-
-

Squats
(30 days)

*Anterior Tibialis (shin muscle)/Calves/Quads/
Hamstrings/Gluteus/Low back/Hip Flexors.*

The squat is a power exercise involving compound
movement, meaning that it requires effort from more
than one muscle group at a time. There are many
ways to perform squats but these are the two I find
most effective.

For the advanced athlete: Squats can be performed
freestyle (without the use of a machine or other
equipment). Weights can be either carried in each
hand or via a weight bar placed behind the head and
across the top of the shoulders.

Stand with the feet shoulder-width apart. There
should be a slight anterior rotation to the hips. The
shoulder blades should be gently squeezed together to
prevent rounding in the back. If you are using a bar,
place your hands outside the shoulders, palms up,

and facing the bar -- arms should form a "football goalpost" position. Contract the abdominal muscles, and breath in as the torso is lowered. Position the body as if you were going to sit back into a chair or stool. Keep weight towards the middle of the feet. Knees must not extend anywhere near the toes. In fact, if this exercise is performed correctly, the knees hardly move at all. The hips should only be lowered to an angle that is greater than 90 degrees to your knees. In other words, do not drop the butt below the height of the knees. Try to be even in the delivery of power through both legs.

Feet shoulder width apart, weight over the middle of feet

Sink hips back, keep back straight

Lower with control, return to start, exhale as you lift

It's a good idea to practice the movement without using any weights at first. Just sit down on a chair or stool and touch the butt down only lightly before lifting back up to the starting position. Maintain, excellent posture (back in extension i.e., shoulder blades contracted not rounded) through the entire movement.

You will notice that the angle between your torso and upper leg at the bottom of the movement is very similar to the angle between the upper and lower leg.

For the novice athlete: This method is recommended not only for novices but also for anyone who has had a history of knee problems or who is in rehab. (It works perfectly well for advanced athletes too). It involves the use of a an exercise ball.

 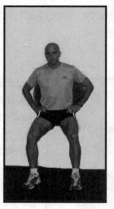

Lower with control

Return to start

Exhale as you straighten

Place the ball behind the small of the back. Lean against a firm flat wall with the ball between back and wall. Adopt the same starting position as described in the first "squats" method. Note however that since the ball is now there for support, it's possible to be more flexible with the placement of the feet. Knees must still be protected by keeping them from extending out beyond the toes. Lower the body down to the same squat position as described in the advanced method.

■ ■ ■ ■ ■ ■ ■ ■ ■ ■

Split Squats or Static Lunge
(All levels)

*Calves, Anterior Tibialis (shin muscles), Quads,
Hamstrings, Gluteus, Hip Flexors*

It is difficult enough to describe this exercise in
person, let alone in a book, but I will give it my best
shot.

*Stride position
shoulders over
hips*

*Lower back knee
to floor; keep front
knee over heel*

Exhale as you lift

Bearing in mind that most of us have one side of our
body that is stronger than the other, this exercise is
designed to address that imbalance as you strengthen
one leg at a time.

Begin in a standing position. Keep the back in
extension. Place a weight in each hand or a light bar
across the shoulders behind the head.

Take a step forward (à la running stride) with one leg.
Bring your center of gravity directly downwards, the
front leg will bend around the knee joint. Again, it is
imperative that the front knee is kept over the ankle,
do not allow the knee to drift towards the toes.

Shoulders remain in alignment over the hips. The back leg will have some bend to it and will be resting on the ball of the back foot. At the bottom of the movement, your back knee will come very close to touching the ground.

You will almost certainly feel an intensity in the front of the back leg in the upper thigh/hip area. This is the stretching of your hip muscles. It is the front leg (specifically the quadriceps) that is providing the power required to first lower the torso down and then raise it back up to the starting position.

Complete the set, switch legs and repeat. Alternatively switch legs upon the completion of two sets, whichever you prefer.

■ ■ ■ ■ ■ ■ ■ ■ ■ ■ ■

Leg Extension
(All levels)

Quadriceps

If performing this exercise in a gym you can work with either a leg extension machine or an exercise ball.

Use a light weight

Raise leg with control

Aim for maximal extension

Squeeze quadriceps muscle

Lower with control

Using the leg extension machine: If you are using a leg extension machine it is best to work one leg at a time. Working with both legs together can compound the imbalance that already exists within our leg musculature since it usually causes the dominant leg to do most of the work. We will proceed using a single leg approach and a very light manageable weight.

Begin with the lower leg at a 90-degree angle to the upper leg. Make sure that the toes are slightly turned out, a position which will accentuate the strengthening of the interior lower quadriceps, known as the VMO (*vastus medialis oblique*). The VMO is the main stabilizer of the knee.

Straighten the lower leg up to the point where it is in line with the upper leg creating a brief maximal contraction of the quadriceps muscles. Lower leg slowly and with control -- return to starting position.

It is important to focus on going through a complete range of motion and a maximal contraction with a one second hold at the top of the movement. This is because the VMO only maximally contracts during the last five degrees of extension. Through experience gained by coaching large numbers of female runners in my women's running group, the "Iron Maidens" of Santa Cruz, California, I can tell you that this lower interior quadriceps is a particularly vulnerable area in the female runner's makeup. By strengthening the VMO, women can go along way towards eliminating the knee and knee-related problems encountered during their running careers.

You should complete 10 to 12 leg extensions per side and then repeat. Or again, you could switch to the second side after completing two sets.

Lower feet toward ground so that lower leg makes a 90-degree angle with the upper legs

Using a medicine ball: Sit on the bench holding the rear edge for support. Perform a double-leg extension by placing a small medicine ball between the feet and following the previous instructions for the single leg extension. Over time, using this method will increase the strength of the hip adductor (interior hip/thigh) stabilizing muscles. This is useful to runners as we rely on these muscles a great deal for stability during forward movement.

Using an exercise ball or bench: If performing this exercise on an exercise ball or bench then adding ankle weights becomes an option. Follow the directions as detailed for the leg extension machine making sure to sit on the ball with excellent posture.

Recommendation for novice runners: I recommend that novice runners complete this exercise twice a week for a total of three weeks before adding more sets to your routine. Since this exercise can prove very effective using nothing but the leg's own weight, you should wait four to six weeks before adding any (light) weights.

∎ ∎ ∎ ∎ ∎ ∎ ∎ ∎ ∎ ∎

Leg Hamstring Curls
(All levels)

Hamstrings

A temperamental muscle group, the hamstrings comprise three major muscles at the back of the upper leg. Originating in the pelvic region and attaching below the knee, they play an integral role in the rotation of the leg and flexion and extension of the knee.

Hamstring injuries vary in severity from minor tears to catastrophic tears that can take months to rehabilitate. My recommended exercises will go along way in helping you to avoid these injuries - but first lets refresh our knowledge as to exactly what happens during the runner's leg cycle and why hamstring injuries are so easily sustained.

If we take a look at the leg cycle, we will see that:

a) the right leg drives off

b) the right leg then progresses through its recovery

c) the right leg then swings through to become the lead leg

d) there is then a point in flight when gravity begins to take over and the right leg moves into its descent and returns to the support phase.

It is during (c) the forward swing phase, that the hamstring is extremely susceptible to injury. Allow me to explain.

1) In the beginning of the leg's flight phase the *lower half* (from the knee to the foot) of the right leg will be *angled behind the upper half.*

2) The upper half of the leg continues on its forward path until it reaches its hinge moment (remember, this is the point at which it can travel no more).

3) The lower half of the leg will swing forward hinged as it is at the knee and it is this swing-through that puts the lower hamstring under extreme duress, its whole role being to decelerate the lower leg (which would otherwise snap like a twig at the knee). There is an eccentric contraction whereby the muscles simultaneously stretch yet contract to slow down the movement of the lower leg as it swings through. It is the forceful nature of this deceleration process that often causes hamstring injuries to occur.

Enjoy the following photos and then we will continue our hamstring discussion...

The author with his coaching partner
Eddy Hellebuyck, 1996 Olympian and the
world's #1 Masters runner at the time
of printing

The author relaxing with friends. To GP's right is
Mbarak Hussein, three-time Honolulu Champion
and 4th place finisher at 2002 Boston Marathon
with a time of 2:09

Flight Phase.
Note angle of left arm and
position of right ankle.

*Coach GP in full flight,
demonstrating good relaxation at
the end of a hard workout -- a little
too much upper body rotation...
hey -- nobody's perfect!*

*Better mechanics
allow you to hunt down
your opponent.*

*Running tall with the "jockey" well
positioned over the "racehorse."
Note strong right arm drive and
corresponding forward motion of the
right leg led by the knee. Also note
simultaneous full extension of the
left, or driving, hip.*

Note the "power pole" -- a term that
refers to the curved line of power
which extends from the tip of the shoulder
through the (excellent) extension of the
drive-off foot. In the above photo this
would apply to the runner's right
hand side. This "power pole", created
as it is with proper running mechanics,
culminates in optimal flight time.

*This out-of-focus photo
clearly shows the relationship
between forward arm and leg.*

Mbarak Hussein in drive-off mode --
note angle of right arm and right leg.

Running well is
"Poetry in Motion."

Mbarak Hussein in full flight.
Note angle of left foot before impact.

*Mbarak during acceleration,
demonstrates proper hip, foot and arm
position at the point of drive-off.*

*Grass is an excellent surface on
which to stride out and generate
some "flight time."*

Hamstrings (continued)

There are three effective, but slightly different, methods for strengthening the hamstring muscles that I want to share with you.

The first - **leg hamstring curls** -- are the most familiar.

Keep hips down on bench

Use light weight, exhale as you lift

Use controlled movement

For most runners the hamstrings will be a good deal weaker than the quadriceps. This is why I recommend selecting a very light starting weight for leg curls. Also make sure to keep your body flat and pressed into the bench. I cannot tell you how many times I have seen athletes who have selected weights that are far too heavy. In order to lift the weight, their bodies launch into a whole series of involuntary compensatory movements, such as the buttocks raising off the bench to help the hip flexors assist in the lift by "shortening up." This is akin to standing upright and trying to bring the heel up to your buttocks while, in the process of raising the heel, bending over at the waist and bringing the knee in the direction of the chest (hip flexion). That is my analogy of what athletes are mistakenly doing when lifting too heavy a weight on the leg curl machine. *Select a weight light enough to allow you to bring your heel towards your buttocks without flexing at the hip.* You can choose to strengthen both legs together, or one at a time. As per the preceding leg exercises, I recommend strengthening each leg individually.

In a gym setting: Lie face down (prone) on a leg curl machine. Starting with your legs straight out behind you, contract your gluteal muscles to protect the back then raise one leg at a time in a smooth controlled manner. Continue raising the leg being sure to complete the full range of motion. Squeeze the hamstring at the top of the movement, then lower with control to the starting position. The non-working leg remains on the bench. Remember to exhale as the leg is raised and inhale as the leg is lowered.

Example of bad form, hips rising off the bench to compensate for too heavy a weight

Complete 10 to 12 leg curls per side and then repeat. As with leg extensions novices should complete this exercise twice a week for a total of three weeks before adding more sets to your routine. Otherwise I recommend one to two sets per leg.

■ ■ ■ ■ ■ ■ ■ ■ ■ ■

For the non-gym setting #1: This hamstring exercise works well with the assistance of an exercise ball.

Lie on your back, legs straight, heels on the ball, hands by hips, palms down. Contract the gluteal and abdominal muscles and press up into a bridge position, using the arms for support.

Lie on back, hands by hips, palms down

Contract gluteal and abdominal muscles

Raise hips up making a straight line between heels and shoulders

Roll ball in with both feet toward gluteus as far as you can, exhale as you roll the ball in

Maintain a stable pelvis

Return to starting position

There should now be a straight line between the heels and the shoulders. Using the strength of your heels and calves, roll the ball towards your gluteus; this should involve maximal contraction of the hamstrings. Return leg to starting position.

The novice athlete should begin by using both legs to perform the exercise. The advanced athlete can place one heel on the ball while holding the other leg straight out about 12 to 18 inches above the ball. The heel on the ball will be placed more centrally. This is a much, much harder exercise. You will feel this exercise intensely in the calf while the abdominal muscles will have to work hard to maintain stability. Begin with one set of ten repetitions and build up from there.

For the non-gym setting #2: The final method for strengthening the hamstrings specifically parallels the running motion in terms of how the hamstring muscles are recruited. This is the kneeling hamstring exercise.

This exercise requires the assistance of a training partner. If that isn't practical for you, then you can try some other methods of anchoring your feet. Tucking the toes under the edge of the couch will often work, as long as your feet remain firmly on the floor throughout the exercise.

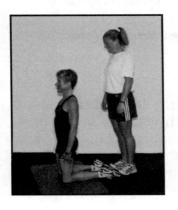

Kneeling upright, secure position by having partner stand on balls of feet

Begin in a kneeling position, with the lower legs at a 90-degree angle to the upper legs. The lower legs should be straight out behind the body with the soles of the feet facing up. Knees, hips and shoulders should all be in alignment. Be sure to maintain good posture with the back remaining in extension (shoulder blades contracted) and the arms by the sides.

Now, to perform the exercise, have your partner stand on the underside of your toes. Keeping your gluteus muscles (buttocks) contracted, lean forward in a fixed manner, maintaining the straight alignment from knee to shoulder (somewhat resembling a downhill ski jumper position).

Hinge forward from the knee, shoulders aligned over hips, back straight

Contract gluteus through movement

Move only a few inches forward

Exhale as you return to starting position

Move very, very slowly. Proceed only to the furthest point (a matter of inches) at which you can still return to the starting position solely by contracting the hamstrings. The stronger the hamstrings, the further you will be able to go. If you begin to cramp up, just place your hands on the floor in front of you and bail out of the movement. Try to make sure you contract the hamstrings with equal force on either side.

Novice athletes should repeat this exercise five to eight times per one set. Advanced athletes can complete two sets of 10 to 12 repetitions. You will need to demonstrate good common sense and judgment as you will be determining your own range of motion (i.e., it will not be predetermined by a machine).

Planning your strength-training

Now you have my top 20 exercises for strength-training specific to running. To be a better runner, you need to run, period. However, the exercises listed here have really helped me and countless athletes that I have worked with, to improve our "chassis and drive trains." They will work for you too.

How much strength-training should you do? I recommend strength-training three days per week with one or more days off between each session, following a three-week mesocycle as shown in the table on page 136. (The term mesocycle will be explained in Mile 16, but in essence means a three-week training period).

3 Week Mesocycle	Week #1	Week #2	Week #3
Day #1	Upper Body & Core Strength	Lower Body & Core Strength	Upper Body & Core Strength
Day #2	Lower Body & Core Strength	Upper Body & Core Strength	Lower Body & Core Strength
Day #3	Upper Body & Core Strength	Lower Body & Core Strength	Upper Body & Core Strength

Note: During specific parts of your training cycles, the racing season for example or if you are within three weeks of a marathon, you will need to adjust your strength-training regimen. There will be times directly pre- and post-marathon for example, where there will be zero strength-training. As always use good common sense when it comes to your training and remember that consistency throughout your training cycle will be the key to your success.

Conclusion

By strengthening your lower, upper and core areas you can increase your lean muscle mass. Since muscle cells require more energy and burn more calories than fat cells, this increases your metabolism even when you are at rest. This has the added benefit of keeping your weight at an optimal level. Furthermore, it increases the tenacity of our soft tissue, including cartilage, tendons and ligaments, it also increases our muscular power, endurance, stamina, coordination and our ability to withstand the overall stresses brought on by the rigors of daily running, training and racing.

Are these the only exercises to do? Absolutely not! There are countless routines, programs, exercise styles and methods. I am simply providing you with the top 20 exercises that, in my experience, are safe, time-efficient and adaptable to either a gym or home setting. They also target areas that are critical to your running fluidity and strength. In strength-training just as in running, it is imperative to have a plan to follow, to know where you have come from, where you are and where it is you are trying to go. Incorporating these exercises as some or all of your plan will help you achieve your running goals while remaining less prone to injury.

Mile 16.0 Don't Exercise...Train!

-
-
-
-

Up until this point in the book I have identified and discussed the basic elements involved in increasing your efficiency and economy as a runner. In addition, you now have an effective and time-efficient strength-training program to complement your running. What follows in this chapter is the discussion of some of the other important components of a well-balanced training program, including motivation, training (or planning) and the always contentious subject of nutrition. By the end of this discussion the reasoning behind the Mile 16.0 chapter heading, "Don't exercise...train!" should become clear.

Desire and Motivation

If you are embarking on a running program, know that desire from within is where it all begins. All of the knowledge gained from the previous chapters will be of use only if you are motivated to get out your door in the first place. There are thousands of athletes still waiting to get started and just as many who exercise inconsistently. How can you avoid being one of them? How can you hold onto your motivation?

In 1972, a young 21-year-old University of Oregon runner by the name of Steve Prefontaine represented the USA at the Munich Olympics in the 5,000 meter final. He was an extremely gifted athlete and supremely confident in spite of the fact that he was more used to racing against his college peers than competing on the world's largest track and field stage, against some of the finest runners in history.

It is well documented now that in a valiant effort, "Pre" gave it his all in his attempt for gold. He was in the lead for much of the race, but in the end was beaten by a very seasoned group of Europeans and settled for an agonizing fourth place. This was a bitter defeat for the young man from Coos Bay, a runner who had become accustomed to winning.

Legend has it that after Prefontaine returned to the United States, his Olympic and university coach Bill Bowerman took him aside after he missed several track practices. He said something to the effect of: "Steve, if you want to be on this team, then show up at 6:00 a.m. for practice and I will give you the workout, otherwise you will not make the team. I cannot coach the desire in you; that must come from within."

Prefontaine did show up for practice. He put his Olympic defeat behind him and went on to hold seven American records in distances ranging from 2,000 to 10,000 meters before his untimely death in May 1975 from a single car crash. This tragedy did not come before Pre had established himself as a legend in the running world, a legend that has only grown stronger over time.

Prefontaine's story serves as an example of desire, motivation and a bloody-minded determination to succeed. If you believe that you can be motivated by outside forces, such as a girlfriend, boyfriend, husband, wife, mother or father, then you are mistaken. Certainly some amount of impetus can be gained from these relationships, but as far as long-term training goes, it will be short-lived. The same can be said of extraneous motives to train, such as exclusively to lose weight, or to look good or to fit in those old jeans.

We are constantly inundated via the electronic and print media, including obnoxious infomercials, with information on how we should look. We should be taller or thinner, have more hair, have less hair, have more sex, eat this food, take that pill -- and so it goes on, in an endless carousel of confusion. The harsh reality is there are no shortcuts, no easy ways to long-term health and fitness. No wonder drug, no magic pill. Neither will you remain motivated and achieve your goals through rudderless exercising. What you need is an intelligent, well-structured training plan: a plan designed to inspire you to complete all the hard work it requires.

Training...not exercising!

Not exercising -- a strange recommendation indeed. Allow me to explain.

While I accept that even without a structured training regimen, regular workouts at your local health club are better than daily visits to a burger house -- they are not enough to guarantee success in reaching your fitness goals over a long period of time, namely your lifetime.

I do not mean to suggest that in order to achieve a high degree of physical fitness, you must be an aspiring Olympian: not at all. I am simply suggesting that whether you are starting a physical fitness program for the first time or restarting one after 20 years of inactivity, you should *follow the proven physiological principles of training that a qualified coach would use in training an aspiring Olympian.* In coaching my age group (amateur) runners, I always try to instill in them the importance of viewing themselves as athletes. If you are willing to forgo the easier option of the recliner in front of the television, get yourself out in all kinds of weather for a specific period of time or distance and measure yourself against the clock, then you are deserving of the title "athlete." This title is not exclusive to those blessed with enough speed to challenge for an Olympic medal. Whatever your age or fitness level, carry yourself as an athlete and make sure you train as an athlete would train!

Exactly how does an athlete train? Well, the ruling principle is as follows: Optimal Stress followed by Optimal Recovery = Optimal Performance. This is known as "The Training Effect" and applies just as much to the novice as to the elite athlete. Athletes refer to this as the "hard easy" method of training.

For example, when we perform a medium to high intensity exercise task, such as an uptempo run, there is a specific stress placed upon the body that is equal to that intensity. After the task is completed, we immediately go into recovery mode and, depending on the intensity and duration of the task, the recovery period could be several hours to several days. During the course of a seven-day training period (often referred to by coaches as a Micro Cycle) a hard training session will be followed by a decrease in fitness over the subsequent 24 hours as the body recovers and regenerates. This regeneration involves a combination of appropriate rest, good nutrition (taking in quality carbohydrates, proteins and fats along with essential minerals and vitamins), proper hydration and light training. This light training might include active isolated stretching and an easy run to assist with muscle soreness and the promotion of blood flow and suppleness throughout the body. The resulting effect is that the human body will rebound stronger and fitter than it was prior to the hard training day.

An important point to make here is that even though there are many factors to be considered in training the human body (training conditions, climate, injury status, etc.), as a general rule if the "hard day, easy day" theory is followed, the athlete is afforded a greater chance of success. On the other hand, if one hard day is followed by another hard day, then the regeneration or recovery period will be seriously impaired. Yes, there are some exceptions to this rule, mainly having to do with the training of elite athletes for competition. These cases notwithstanding, it is extremely inadvisable for either the novice or the age group runner to make a habit of putting in consecutive hard training days. To do so will prevent the steady recovery and regeneration that is essential for the continued "climb up the fitness ladder" through the body's physiological preparation for the next hard training session. Without this recovery, the results inevitably lead to over-training, injury and poor health.

For all the above reasons...don't just exercise...train!

The Chess Match and The Plan

Earlier in this chapter I discussed motivation and the fact that extrinsic motivational factors such as wanting to look good or wishing to please someone else, very rarely, if ever, work over a sustained period of time. With no plan of action, a plateau will inevitably be reached, frustration will set in, enjoyment will be reduced and the goal will be abandoned. Even with best of intentions, it's easy to get caught in this rudderless trap time and time again.

How to avoid the trap? Try thinking of your training in terms of a chess match. In this match your body is always awaiting your next move, after which it can react accordingly. The knowledge and understanding of the nature of this chess match is the intangible element separating the athlete from the "weekend warrior" or "workout rat." The weapon that is used by the athlete to win the chess match is known as periodization, or the training plan.

Periodization is a term that appears regularly in texts on running and is used extensively in high school and college programs as well as at the club and professional level. To some extent it is an elitist term meaning "to train for a defined period of time with a beginning, middle and end." Basically it means methodical organized training for a predetermined clearly defined period of time, allowing for the appropriate adaptation to stress (training) and leading to a goal event. This goal event might be the completion of a local race or a circuit of your neighborhood block, by a specific date.

To achieve success as an athlete, in other words to achieve the benefits of long-term health and fitness, "periodization," or a training plan, is the key. Break down short, mid- and long-term goals into bite size amounts -- the plan must contain specific daily goals. That way each day leads to the next, each week leads to the next and each training cycle leads to the next, all the way up to the main goal. Once the goal (a race, perhaps) has been undertaken, there is an appropriate recovery period, then new goals are set and the cycle begins again.

As far as motivation is concerned, it is the progressively challenging nature of the goals, each requiring the body's appropriate adaptation, that will keep you continually reaching for new levels of success. Particularly motivational will be the short-term goals, and even when you fall short of a goal from time to time (as we all do), they will keep you motivated as you search yourself for a way to achieve that missed goal in the next attempt. This motivation, however, will not endure if you are training for the wrong reasons, as previously mentioned. In these cases, adherence is really in jeopardy and more often than not, the training ceases.

The Elements of a Plan

Plan Element #1: The training log

A training log serves as a mine of information that can be used for diagnostic purposes with regard to our running, giving immediate feedback on the current state of body and mind. Without it we are traveling blind: we have no records to remind us of how we got here and no compass to keep us on a course to our destination. With it, we can look at our history and make any necessary adjustments to help us along the way towards our goal. Reasonably priced training logs (usually in the $8 to $10 range) are available at all good running stores and sports outlets. They are often packed with training tips and pace charts that may help you towards your goal.

Plan Element #2: Short-term, mid-term and long-term goals

These goals will be the foundation of your success:

Short-term:

Time frame: Goal within 1-2 weeks
Examples: Completion of a local race or one
                continuous loop of your neighborhood.

Mid-term:

Time frame: Goal within 2-6 months.

Examples: To run a local race without stopping or to break a certain time for one mile on the track.

Long-term:

Time frame: Goal could be from within six months to several years.

Examples: Completion of a marathon, walking a charity walk over several days or training for the next Olympics.

As far as your goals are concerned the possibilities are infinite, but it is the long-term goal that glows in the distance, while the short- and mid-term goals light up the path along the way.

Plan Element #3: Training periods

Unit: A specific interval or workload within a training session.

Session: A singular or individual training session.

Microcycle: A shorter segment of your training program. Typically seven days.

Mesocycle: An intermediate segment of your training program, often allowing enough time for one adaptation period. (The length of time required, physiologically speaking, to benefit from a given workout). This is typically 14 to 21 days.

Macrocycle: A longer period of time often described as your training season. For example, a cross country season or summer time racing season for 5K/10K races or, very often, the overall training period leading up to and including a half-marathon or marathon race. Typically two to three months and sometimes longer.

Plan Element #4: Quality or up tempo workouts

As previously mentioned, success in training comes from a combination of hard and easy days. I want to examine the terminologies of some of these "up tempo" runs so that we can see which type of run falls into which category.

Aerobic conditioning:

This would be your easy day. A fun run with no requirement for running at a fast pace. It is conversational and can range in duration from 30 minutes to three hours depending on racing goal, location in training period and ability. This run is designed to improve the body's ability to withstand the impact forces of running and to improve its efficiency at metabolizing stored fat for fuel.

Interval training:

A series of faster repetitions (usually at a set race pace or paces) for a predetermined distance and/or time followed by a predetermined recovery period by time and/or distance. For example, 10 repeats of 400 meters at 5K race pace with a 60 second jog between each repeat.

Fartlek runs:

Fartlek (the Swedish word for speed play) is an uptempo or higher intensity workout randomly selected over varying distances, times and paces. Usually the length of time of the fartlek run ranges from a matter of seconds to a couple of minutes.

Anaerobic conditioning:

In all endurance events there is both aerobic and anaerobic energy contribution. Anaerobic production has two sources:

1) Alactate. Maximal force running. An energy system that endures for eight to nine seconds.

2) Anaerobic Glycolytic. An energy source that occurs above 65 percent VO2 Max. VO2 Max is the highest rate of oxygen utilization that can be achieved during maximal levels of exercise. Research has shown that this can be improved with endurance training.

Training between 65 and 85 percent VO2 Max is termed "training at your lactate threshold." Specific running at these intensities will improve the breakdown of glycogen as a substrate (a fuel source for energy metabolism). This allows the runner to go further and faster before being hindered by the accumulation of lactic acid, a by-product of anaerobic energy production.

Hill repeats:

A series of faster repetitions (usually at a set race pace or paces) for a predetermined time and/or distance followed by a predetermined recovery period time and/or distance. They can range in length from 30 seconds to several minutes. The shorter the repeat, the higher the intensity of the running. Hill repeats build tremendous strength in the muscles and the skeletal system, increasing the power output of the heart along with improving the economy and the efficiency of the stride.

An example might be 10 repeats of a 30-second acceleration up a hill at 5K race effort with a 60-second jog between each repeat. Hill repeats usually last for a cycle of four to six weeks. There may be as many as two to three cycles of four to six weeks, run once per week in a macrocycle, depending on the level of athlete.

Cardiovascular:

Writing a book primarily examining the biomechanical aspects of running, I do not intend to cover all the aspects of cardiovascular training. Further comprehensive information on human performance as affected by training the cardiopulmonary system can be found in many books on performance physiology such as *Training Distance Runners* by Coe and Martin.

Which plan is right for me?

Finding the right training program for you is essential if you are to succeed at your sport. Many resources are available to get you started on creating your own plan. You can refer to books such as *Training Distance Runners* as mentioned above or *Workouts for Working People* by legendary Ironman Triathletes Mark Allen and Julie Moss. Contact your local running club, running store or running coaches for this kind of information and finally, you can use the Internet, a tremendous running resource.

Use these sources to look at your goals and work out your plan. Remember that no matter what your goals might be, your plan should closely match your current ability, but should also incorporate an ample degree of challenge. Make sure that your goals can only be achieved through consistent training. If the plan is too easy, you will not maximize its benefits; if it is too hard then at best you may lose motivation, and at worst you run the risk of injury.

A good basic plan should incorporate aerobic type running, speed work, strength-running, strength-training and work on your range of motion and flexibility. There are a couple of hard and fast rules to consider in your plan. Do not increase your mileage by more than five percent per week and do not use more than 10 percent of your weekly mileage in speed work (novices) or up to 20 percent for advanced runners.

What follows are some examples of a seven-day
training plan as provided for three of my athletes. As
you will see, their schedules vary widely but the basic
elements remain the same:

The table on the following page shows a schedule for a
novice/intermediate female runner in her mid-40s
who is returning to consistent running at the start of a
new season.

Schedule #1: Novice/Intermediate Female Runner

Mesocycle #1 Week #1	The agenda for this mesocycle is consistency plus a v. slight increase in endurance. Pay attention to your breathing rhythm as discussed, this will help you later on as the schedule becomes more complex. Our goal in wks 1-3 is to hit 90-95% of the schedule. We are training via heart rate for phase 1. The key is to develop your body's ability to recover efficiently while on the move. This will be achieved through continuous steady state (even pace) running at a moderate effort with little/no recovery.	
Monday	Off. Relax and stretch.	
Tuesday	Easy 3.5 miles of running, relaxed run tall and with good posture and good form, think about your mechanics, the way you carry your arms and your relaxed breathing.	Heart rate building to no higher than 140bpm on this run.
Wed	Off. Relax, rest and stretch today.	Possible yoga class.
Thurs	Morning run, 30 minutes Evening run. 30 minutes	Heart rate < 140bpm Heart rate < 150bpm
Fri	Off. Stretch, hydrate.	
Sat	Track: 1 mile warm up (opposite direction, clockwise-middle lanes, very easy pace). 1 mile strides (4 laps-anti clockwise) jog turns, stride straights in 25 seconds. The workout is: 800m in 2.05 per lap (8.20 mile pace) 400m in 2.00 for lap (8.00 min pace) 2000m in 2.08 per lap (8.32 pace) 400m in 1.59 per lap (7.56 pace).	This is to stimulate your central nervous system and to physiologically prepare you for the workout. Take a 1 lap easy jog between each interval. Focus on good pacing and good breathing technique.
Sun	7 mile run. Run tall, good posture, think about your mechanics.	Heart rate to no higher than 140 bpm.

Schedule #2: Advanced female runner recovering from injury.

Mesocycle #8 Week #1	Training schedule for a thirty year old female runner, capable of running a sub 19 minute 5K. This runner is recovering from injury, so her schedule consists entirely of cross-training.	
Monday	Off. Relax, stretch, hydrate.	
Tuesday	20 mile bike ride include 4 x 3 minute medium intensity accelerations, leave time for a cool down ride at the finish.	Average heart rate 140 bpm, reaching 155 during accelerations
Wed	Elliptical machine, 30 minutes. Low intensity, paralleling an easy run.	Keep heart rate below 145bpm
Thurs	Pool: 250 yard warm up swim then aqua jog 2 sets. Accelerations Effort Recovery 1 minute Mile 30 seconds 2 minutes 5K 30 seconds 3 minutes 5K 30 seconds 3 minutes 5K 30 seconds 2 minutes 5K 30 seconds 1 minute Mile End workout 100 yard easy swim to cool down after aqua jog.	
Fri	Elliptical machine, 40 minutes of easy training, paralleling a 40 minute easy run.	Keep heart rate below 145bpm
Sat	Tempo elliptical....45 minutes total. Warm up for 15 minutes at a low intensity. Then do a steady state tempo equating to 15 minutes of running at threshold effort (10k pace + 15 secs. per mile). Cool down for 15 minutes at the end of the tempo.	Heart rate below 130 bpm Work on good posture and excellent breathing.
Sun	Bike for 90 minutes at a steady state effort. Then hydrate, stretch and rest.	Keep heart rate below 145bpm

Schedule #3: Elite male runner.

Mesocycle #4 Week #3	Training schedule for a twenty-five year old elite male athlete, during the speed endurance and stamina phase of his training.	
Monday	Off. Relax, stretch, hydrate.	
Tuesday	Usual 2 mile warm up and mile of strides. Workout: 4 x 150/50 jog 400 jog 7 x 1000 metres 'in and out' pace Paces 40/30 400 jog between sets 4 mile cool down	Pace 22.5 secs Maintain the 0.5 second tolerance. Maintain excellent breathing and good controlled balance. Stay focused.
Wed	a.m. 6 miles easy running. Stretch, hydrate. p.m. 4 miles mid-pace	
Thurs	Jog to hill 16 x 60secs @ 5K effort, 2 minutes recovery. Return to track, 1 mile in 4:45 4 mile cool down	Pay close attention to relaxation of upper body. Drive the arms and generate efficient knee drive.
Fri	10 mile recovery run. Stretch, hydrate, rest and get to sleep early.	
Sat	Tempo run. Warm up 2 miles easy., move smoothly to 5:45 pace for 1 mile,. Slow to 6:30 pace for 2 minutes,. Return to 5:30 pace for remainder of fourth mile, then jog easy two minutes. Then run 10 x 20 seconds at 4:40 pace with 30 sec jog between. After last one, jog 2 minutes, then run 3 miles at 5:15 pac. Cool down 2 miles to finish.	
Sun	75 - 80 minutes at a low heart rate. Steady state effort. Hydrate, stretch and rest afterwards.	Keep heart rate below 145bpm

These are three completely different schedules. They each have a plan, an agenda designed to lead from one day to the next, from one week to the next and from one mesocycle to the next until ultimately arriving at the main goal. After that main goal has been undertaken and regardless of whether or not it was attained, it is time for recovery and rest before embarking on the next challenge. This is how the cycle of training continues.

Following a race I recommend one easy day of running per mile raced before attempting anything up tempo. Thus your plan should specify three easy days following a 5K, six easy days following a 10K, 26 easy days following a marathon, and so on.

As I have said, use all the resources available to you in developing your own goals and your own training plan. (For more detailed information on how to receive personalized training schedules such as the examples in this book, you can either send an email to runtallruneasy@aol.com or visit our website at www.runningbuzz.com).

Training as an athlete..."True stories"

At this point in this chapter, I would like to share a couple of stories that exemplify the planning principles we have discussed. Having worked with more than a thousand runners, it was hard to single out the stories of only two. There are very many inspirational anecdotes to relate, some of which have reached almost "lore" status amongst local runners. Nevertheless I finally selected the stories of a David*

The stories are real but the names have been changed.

from Santa Cruz, California and a Caroline* who trains with me in New Jersey.

David

For many years now I have coached community track twice a week, on Tuesdays and Saturdays. Approximately six years ago David came to the track on the recommendation of another inspiring athlete Dina* (a lady who overcame many personal obstacles and went on to enjoy a tremendous running career). At that time David weighed close to 400 pounds and worked full time at a sedentary job in the computer industry. His health was in serious jeopardy. However, David had been a runner in high school and he wanted to be strong enough to take up running once again. His ultimate goal was to run the "Wharf to Wharf" race (a very popular six-mile race in Santa Cruz, California) within two years. I immediately began helping him with his training program, starting with a regular regimen of walking on hills at lunchtime and once weekly walking on the track. Our short-term goals were to get his weight under control, to increase his metabolic rate, to improve his self-esteem and to improve his cardiovascular fitness to the point where he was able to walk one continuous mile.

I asked David to consider himself an athlete at all times: think, believe, walk and carry himself as an athlete. This was extremely important, as taking the attitude of an athlete, he would then hold himself accountable to his training goals and make better decisions in all aspects of his life, ranging from the food he ate, the people he associated with and the hours of sleep he needed. It would make the process of training toward his goals much easier to sustain. It would serve as a protective shield, a shining reminder during moments of weakness that he must remain true to his higher purpose and to place himself, every day, in the position to perform at the very best of his ability.

David trained in a methodical progressive manner and showed steady improvement, overcoming setbacks such as sore knees, to the point where he could eventually walk one mile. After that we introduced small elements of running, starting with just one mile of jogging the straights on the track (100 meters) while walking the 100 meters on the turns.

We attacked David's fitness from two angles. One was to work on improving his stamina by having him continue to walk longer distances and by slowly increasing the distances he could run. We were very careful not to push too fast too soon. Once we were comfortable with both his fitness level and his weight, the other angle was through the introduction of some "quality" running. We began with short elements of faster running. These were designed to improve his strength and power, to streamline the efficiency and the economy of his mechanics and, most importantly, to increase his sense of enjoyment and self-worth.

In July 2002 David not only completed the "Wharf to Wharf" six-mile race, but he ran the entire distance. He has lost over 150 pounds and at the time of writing is considering a career change into law enforcement.

▪ ▪ ▪ ▪ ▪ ▪ ▪ ▪ ▪ ▪

Caroline

As a guest speaker at various venues across the United States, I am fortunate enough to encounter runners from all walks of life, of all ages and all abilities.

I met Caroline after speaking at a local hospital in New Jersey in the spring of 2002. The content of my talk was representative of much of the content of this book, including my thoughts on behaving as an athlete at all times. Caroline was in her late 30s, somewhat overweight and in dire need of motivation and structure. She was a recently divorced single parent who worked full-time. Shortly after my lecture Caroline decided to attend one of our Jersey Shore Stingers track workouts.

Caroline told me that several years earlier in her life she had been able to run three or four miles at a time but that she had allowed herself to get out of the habit of exercising and had further allowed herself to be influenced by a partner was not enthusiastic about exercise. The end result was a young woman who was extremely frustrated with her present condition. It was time for a change.

Having reiterated to Caroline that she must think, feel and behave like an athlete at all times, we immediately set about establishing, short-, mid- and long-term goals. We designed a weekly training plan (taking into consideration her lifestyle, busy schedule and current fitness level) that would encourage both adherence and progress. The short-term goal was to establish a routine of consistency, in other words to create a positive habit. Her mid-term goal was to turn out for track once to twice per week and walk in increments of a half lap at a time (200 meters) with appropriate rest following each 200-meter interval.

Once Caroline had progressed as far as walking one continuous mile without discomfort, we introduced running for a distance of 100 meters and walking an equal distance for recovery. Again, when Caroline was ready we adopted the same two-pronged "distance and quality" attack that I had employed with David.

To attain her long-term goals of optimal weight and ongoing functional fitness, Caroline will need to practice proper nutrition and follow a well designed training program. This program will allow her, at any given time, to increase intensity for a short pre-determined period in order to peak for a local race such as a 5K or 10K. She will not have to try to remain in peak fitness at all times. The key element is to maintain long-term functional strength and a cardiovascular fitness level that can be "ramped up" in intensity over a few weeks in order to focus on a race that piques her interest and motivation. It is essential to have race goals such as this to keep us motivated through the more difficult days of training such as the short days and long nights of winter. Just one year after starting her new training program Caroline successfully completed a five mile run without stopping.

∎ ∎ ∎ ∎ ∎ ∎ ∎ ∎ ∎ ∎

Returning to the idea of the training plan, in the cases of both David and Caroline, we used progressive systematic training, allowing for adaptation to the stresses placed on them. The plan cycles were as follows:

Microcycle: The seven-day training cycle.

Mesocycle: The three-week training plan. (A critical period of time as it takes approximately three weeks to achieve the benefit of a particular workout).

Macrocycle: In the case of David this goal was originally over a year away but with periodization (microcycles, mesocycles) there were smaller achievable "bite size" steps designed to keep him motivated and on course. As discussed in the case of Caroline, this was to achieve her optimal weight and ongoing functional fitness. We used a 12-month annual plan as her macrocycle.

As discussed above...

Both David and Caroline had specific workouts each week, incorporating hard and easy training days of varying distances and intensities. We made sure to include adequate recovery days and cross training days (an alternative source of cardiovascular training from that of their primary sport designed to give relief from the impact of running) as well as a regimen of strength-training and days off.

So, now we know that a training plan or cycle has a predefined period of time, contains short-, mid- and long-term goals and includes training at varying intensities in order to stimulate physical adaptation to its highest level. We can also feel very confident that with regard to our health and these training plans, all roads lead in the same direction, namely to a stronger and more efficient heart. In fact, the benefits from this type of exercise include, among others, lower stress levels, improved cholesterol levels, reduced risk of heart disease, reduced blood pressure, reduced risk of type 2 diabetes, decreased weight and better body composition.

How far we choose to drive our training depends on many variables -- genes, age, health history, diet, stress levels, climate, time and motivation. No matter what type of athlete you are and no matter how you choose to plan your schedule, the principles of stress and recovery type training will remain true. Remember "Optimal Stress followed by Optimal Recovery = Optimal Performance" and you'll be positioning yourself to achieve all of your goals.

Food and "The Body"

The subject of nutrition is perhaps the most confusing, frustrating aspect of training and living, period! I believe that this is caused by misinformation, inaccuracy and quite often pure and simple intent to mislead. What follows is, I hope, a basic, real life, "in the trenches" explanation of why we are what we eat and why proper fuelling is essential to performance as a runner.

Generally the human body does not like to be stressed. For this very reason, when stress is applied to the body (in the form of exercise) it responds by actually improving itself. During post-stress recovery, the body functions in self-adjustment mode, rebuilding itself to be even stronger than before. It's almost as if little elves come out at night while you are sleeping and rebuild the castle so that it is better prepared for the task at hand next time around. Your "rebuilt" body will now be able to cope with that particular level of stress and discomfort in a much more comfortable and relaxed way.

Similarly, the human body is not in favor of giving up large amounts of fat. It works on the principle that the last meal you ate maybe the last meal it will receive in a while. Now, remember that one of the body's primary functions is temperature regulation, particularly surrounding the vital organs -- so it will give up on sugar, protein and just about anything else before it will part company with its fat storage. This is one of the key reasons why deprivation diets simply do not work. The body is way too clever and it slows your metabolism down to a snail's pace in order to preserve precious energy...stored fat! If you exercise at the same level on a consistent basis, your chess match will have reached a stalemate. Your body will have become extremely efficient at handling the workload placed upon it, burning the least amount of energy that it can get away with. This is why you need to exercise at varying intensities, continually challenging the body to reinvent itself by becoming fitter and stronger, so that it increases its capacity to handle greater workloads. Then, you need to feed the beast enough food, so that it doesn't panic, thinking it is not going to get enough fat! Thus the cycle continues. Let's review from the body's perspective...

My life (my body) living with "Human"...

"I am being challenged (exercised...) I am uncomfortable...I don't like this... I have to become lighter so that I can accomplish this new task as efficiently as possible -- so that I am comfortable... ah! but to achieve that, "Human" will starve me...a double whammy (extra stress and less food...) so I will give up everything else-protein, carbohydrates, tissue -- give it all up so that I can keep my fat reserves for warmth...then when I become comfortable at the task, I can stabilize my metabolism and become very efficient. I can sneer at "Human" as he is now exercising at a comfortable level for me...I can achieve the new task with my slower metabolism and while still retaining decent levels of fat. What's that? "Human" is upping the intensity...hmmm...a chess match eh? OK, back to regenerating myself, improving my performance so that I am comfortable... still I wish I was lighter...well, better give up some more sugar and muscle to jettison some weight, make myself lighter. I cannot afford to give up those fat stores, who knows what "Human" will be up to next, exercising me like a mad dog on one hand and doubling up with a low calorie diet on the other...I'll show "Human"!!

But wait a minute, what's this? Now "Human" is feeding me good quality food and in generous amounts, decent amounts of carbohydrates and proteins, good vitamins for chemical stabilization and minerals for my bones and other important chemical reactions and best of all enough fat (good kind) to satisfy my needs. Now I feel balanced. Now if I have to perform harder and harder tasks (workouts) with adequate recovery/rebuilding times, but I receive enough of the fuel I need...well, then, now in order to be lighter, to be more efficient and comfortable during the chess match, I can afford to burn some fat. Burning some fat will help me weigh less so that I am more comfortable under stress. Since "Human" is feeding me the proper nutrition for survival, in sufficient amounts for me to retain as much as I need to protect my organs, then I guess it won't hurt to give up a few pounds of fat... and checkmate! Now I am a lean mean running machine!"

That is it, runners, oh yes, there may be more scientific descriptions, mostly designed to confuse you. I dare say that there are more eloquent descriptions of the combined effects of training and nutrition, but they can be very hard to follow. (Mostly written by scientists who do a great job, but may not really understand the mindset of an athlete). Nor do they seem to understand the nutrition confusion that is out there -- the fundamental lack of understanding of how the physiology of the human body works as it pertains to exercise and being fed. Hopefully, with my breakdown from the body's perspective, a few of these questions may have been answered and clouds of confusion lifted!

Conclusion

The conclusion to this mile is that if the motivational fire is to remain burning, then the desire for improvement must come from within. Many outside forces that influence us for fleeting moments and motivate us on a short-term basis but the interior drive must be the force to keep us pushing onward during good times and bad. We must be mindful of the fact that the human body is an intricate and amazing machine. If we want to improve that machine there are no short cuts and no easy routes to success -- just good, honest and ultimately rewarding hard work. We must also take into consideration the established principles of training whereby our workouts challenge us just enough to keep us coming back from more but not so hard that we risk injury and over-training. It is this sequential programming, the training in cycles, that allows our bodies to adapt and improve on a consistent basis, giving us a sneak preview with each new level into rewards yet unknown.

Just as with the automobile which, alas, without proper gasoline, will go nowhere, so it is with us runners. We may be highly motivated and highly organized with our training plan all laid out in front of us, but if we continue to ignore the natural human requirement for proper fuel and the maintenance of sound nutritional habits, our training will be doomed before we take our first step.

Speaking of the first step, you might be wondering how best to make use of all this information. I recommend, in this order, that you set about creating good fueling habits and then move on to establishing your short-, mid- and long-term goals. Once done, immediately start developing your own training plan along the guidelines in this chapter. You can either use a computer program or one of the many versatile training logs available online or at your local running store. Remember you need to build from week to week, incorporating hard and easy recovery training days.

Over several mesocycles (approximately three weeks of training to one mesocycle), what were formerly your hard days will become your current easy days and your easy pace will eventually develop into what you once considered your intermediate pace. With the addition of some training races along the way, your workouts should continue to build all the way up to your main goal (completion of the macrocycle).

After the goal event is completed, you should enjoy a period of complete rest and recovery known as your off-season. During that time, you can plan out your next season and, with good judgment, you can determine what paces and distances you should begin with at the of start your next program. I recommend that you begin at the distances and intensities that you had reached at about two-thirds of your way through your previous season. This way you will be continuing to progress rather than beginning each season at the same level. This progression will afford you the opportunity to keep striving towards new levels of fitness and speed. Remember as you become fitter and faster, so the increments of improvement become smaller and smaller, but the rewards are just as great. What it all boils down to is this...

Don't exercise...train!

Mile 17.0
Run Tall, Run Easy, Getting Out of Trouble

●

●

●

●

Running is an extraordinary combination of physics and biology that produces one of the most amazing phenomena in evolution: the artistry and poetry in motion of the living creature. Unlike the crude machines that humans create, there are no squeaks, no rattles, no grinding of artificial materials.

In the context of running as a sport, the title "getting out of trouble" refers specifically to the effective management of difficulty and discomfort brought on by physiological and or psychological stress.

Examples of physiological stress are:

❑ running too fast and out of control, causing a rapid deterioration in the working ability to complete the task at hand
❑ lack of fuel or hydration at the end of a long run
❑ running uphill
❑ running in adverse weather conditions such as heat, cold, humidity or high winds

Examples of psychological stress or difficulty are:

- awareness of slowing down
- fear of slowing down
- negative thinking, lack of motivation to continue, wanting to quit
- increasing anxiety from physical discomfort
- fear of the remaining distance in run or race
- mental fatigue

These are just a few examples. We all have our own particular demons in this area, so please feel free to add yours to the list. Basically anytime our running is negatively impacted, we can consider ourselves to be "in trouble."

After we take a closer look at some of the difficulties we might face in our daily runs, we will return to my "Fab Four," my tried and true methods designed to enhance relaxation, increase efficiency and most importantly to help get you out of trouble when trouble arrives. Once you have successfully employed these methods you will find that they can serve not only to improve the psychological aspect of your runs, but also to increase your motivation to get out the door, confident in the knowledge that you will be better equipped to deal with discomfort when it comes along.

Running...in or out of trouble?

In order for the human body to achieve locomotion thousands of occurrences take place every second. A complex sequence of events that culminate in seamless movement.

The faster the pace in running, the more intense and frenetic are the "behind the scenes" physiological actions required to create forward movement. Yet often up to a point, the faster the running, the more relaxed the runner may appear to the observer, particularly a very talented runner in the early stages of a workout or race.

How can this be? There are several possible reasons.

Internally, when at an accelerated pace, the human body is performing at very high intensity. The heart and lungs are pumping at or close to maximum capacity, the central nervous system is at full voltage, the muscles are rapidly contracting and expanding, and the bones are moving fast. At this higher speed there is a heightened state of awareness. Subconsciously the body performs all the necessary functions more efficiently than usual and for a short time the runner can actually become a more efficient runner without even realizing it. Hence the reason the aforementioned runner appearing to be more relaxed at speed. The essence of this book is to teach you the to *consciously* make these changes in order to permanently enhance your running.

Running can be a very challenging sport. It is fun, yes, but fun in a very strange way. How else can you explain a sport that keeps you looking forward to your run all day, then when you finally get to experience it, keeps you looking at your watch because, frankly, you cannot wait for it to end? I am not suggesting that every run is like this, but if you are honest with yourself, you will agree that quite a few fall into this category.

The love/hate relationship that most if not all of us share with running is perhaps a testament to its difficulty as a sport. Quite often, making the decision to head out the door to your local park, trail, road, mountain range, beach or track is the hardest commitment to make. I am not sure that athletes in many other sports experience the constant mind games that are associated with our everyday running. I know that swimmers, cyclists and triathletes among others experience these same emotions. Many other athletes however, do not. Soccer, tennis or golf enthusiasts, to name a few, do not have to bribe themselves to get out the door in order to participate in their favorite sport on a regular basis.

Again, I am not suggesting for one second that these sports do not require nerves or create butterflies in their players, as they most certainly do. The difference is the anguish and anticipation that runners experience in connection with the physical and psychological pain that running often produces. After all, each and every day that we run, we are challenged to overcome both physical and mental obstacles. These obstacles range in degree of difficulty. While the motion or movement of running is linear the physiological and psychological aspects are definitely not.

A fascinating aspect to running and one that produces a strong kindred spirit among its participants is that no one group is excluded from difficulty. The pains are not restricted to the hard efforts of a track workout or race and it is just as common for an elite runner in peak racing shape to feel miserable during an everyday recovery run as runners at the novice or intermediate level. Continuing in this vein, just how is it that on a run-of-the-mill midweek five-miler at two minutes per mile slower than our current 10K race pace, we feel worse than we did the previous weekend racing in a local 10K at that two minutes per mile faster pace?

While many of these difficult running days can be attributed to poor nutrition, inadequate hydration, sleep deprivation and other physical limitations or restrictions, I also believe that the answer lies somewhere deep in the mysterious magic of this ancient sport.

As difficult as running can sometimes be, it can also be an effortless, flowing, relaxing and euphoric symphony of movement. These types of runs, the runs when we are "firing on all cylinders," are usually all too infrequent. As runners, our attempts to "get in the zone" closely resemble a search for the Holy Grail. Why is it then that a sport which has so many participants and which can at times be so utterly torturous, has prompted so few people to work on improving their form and biomechanics? Strange too is the fact that in comparison to cardiovascular/pulmonary developmental books or training guides, very little has even been written on the subject of running biomechanics.

Golf and tennis represent only two of the many sports whose enthusiasts are willing to invest a great deal of time in working on their "game" by learning, practicing and perfecting the fundamentals. Yet runners, for the most part, remain oblivious to the tremendous improvements to be gained through developing and refining their biomechanical proficiency.

I am not alluding to the hard tempo, fartlek, long runs and track workouts that you do. I am referencing the very essence of physically moving your body step-by-step across the ground. This is the biomechanics of running, the contraction of the muscles required to facilitate the optimal forward movement of your skeletal system.

Coach GP's Fab Four: A review

Now is the time to return to my "Fab Four" as detailed at the end of certain key chapters in this book. I am not suggesting that once you incorporate the following four elements into your running it will all be easy from there. Far from it. However, they will provide the necessary tools to get you home or to the end of your race. (If nothing else, they will keep your mind occupied and those negative thoughts at bay). The Fab Four will get you out of trouble.

Fab #1: *Run Tall.*

Remember, whether you are on a neighborhood jog or a peak season race, the taller you are relative to your own height, the better your running will be. You must get your hips up. The jockey must sit atop the horse with proper upright posture.

Fab #2: *Foot Strike.*

With proper foot strike you will be better able to generate drive-off force with your "take-off leg," therefore maintaining your preferred flight time. This in turn allows three more things to happen:

a) You will have precious extra milliseconds in flight for your working muscles to relax.

b) The longer flight time will result in a more complete leg cycle. The front foot will be able to land closer to a point directly below your center of gravity (helping you remain taller).

c) The improved drive-off also results in faster foot speed, bringing the heel up behind the body (closer to your hips, remember metronome, weight closer to point of axis!) and providing a faster, smoother leg action. This in turn generates more speed, the speed helps your flight time and thus the cycle continues.

Fab #3: *Arm Drive.*

It is impossible to maintain efficient running biomechanics (maximal flight time) without proper arm drive. The arm drive provides the counter thrust to help drive the lead leg of the corresponding side with enough lift and force to fly through the air in an optimal manner. How do you know what that optimal manner is? You don't have to, because during the course of your training runs -- runs that are performed at specific accurate paces -- your arm drive will develop its own optimal cadence for a given pace. All that is left for you to do is to start your races or training runs at the right pace for your given distance and maintain the arm drive that your arms set for themselves at the beginning of the run.

Fab #4: *Breathing.*

It is essential during times of difficulty, be it physiological and psychological, that you get in synch with your body's natural breathing rhythm and run to that rhythm or cadence. The horse and jockey must be at one with each other. Pay attention and you will notice that your breathing rhythm keeps time with your foot strike. This is a very powerful safety net, and it will keep you more relaxed and inwardly focused, taking your mind away from negative thoughts and ideas. Your breathing rhythm is the conductor keeping time in a tremendous cascading symphony.

Conclusion

Running is a very simple and enjoyable sport but it can turn very challenging when trouble strikes. Applying the "Fab Four" above will ensure that you are well equipped to handle difficulties as they arise. There are many components to a well-balanced training program, but in the sport of running unless the integrity of your musculoskeletal system is well-maintained, it is just a matter of time before your performance is compromised.

Reflections of a Coach
The Summary

-

-

-

-

In the past, coaching and other popular sources of running information have focused amost exclusively on the cardiopulmonary aspects of training. This old-fashioned approach is slowly giving way to the ideas that form follows function, and that function can be changed with skillful assessment, redirection and teaching. There is a skill to running that can be practiced and honed over time.

Prior to the 1970s, coaching was mainly restricted to elite runners. The recreational boom had yet to take place. From the mid-70s to the mid-90s, coaching began to reach a wider audience and clubs began forming across the United States. Coaching was for the most part performed by former elite runners from the high school, college or professional ranks. These coaches may have received some instruction in biomechanics, but more often than not, they worked from a 'more running is better' philosophy. Thousands of new recreational runners took up this philosophy, and subsequently followed this methodology in their own training.

It was not long before an explosion of recreational sports injuries occurred, an increase that the medical profession has struggled to handle. The result in this new wave of injuries? Whole new areas of healthcare known collectively as Sports Medicine.

In the early part of the 21st century as major marathons and other races continue to grow, quality coaching is more important than ever. Often inspired by charity organizations, friends, or relatives who have completed a race, more and more people are taking to running for the first time.

Certain members of the medical profession maintain that running is bad for you, or that it causes injuries. This is far from true. It is poor biomechanics and an inferior musculoskeletal system that lead to running injuries.

I do not deny that a certain section of the human population is predisposed genetically in such a fashion that would make it advisable for them to consider a different sport. Perhaps one that is non-load bearing, such as swimming or cycling. This notwithstanding, all others can benefit greatly from a solid foundation of professional coaching on how to be a well-balanced athlete. Coaching would include instruction in progressive training with optimal recovery time, range of motion and flexibility, nutrition and hydration and sufficient hours of rest and sleep.

Of prime importance would be instruction in the art of proper running biomechanics to insure that you are moving your body through space in the most economical, efficient and powerful manner possible.

Remember, run to the maximum height relative to your own height.

In short, "Run Tall, Run Easy."

See you on the roads and trails...

Coach GP

Acknowledgments:

The information in this book has been acquired over many years and I am still learning more each day. Running is a way of life for me and as such it has afforded me many wonderful memories and many wonderful friends without whom this book simply would never have happened. These are some of the very important people who have woven the tapestry of my life and to whom I am eternally grateful.

Family

To my sister Nicole and brother-in-law Mason, whose combined wisdom reaches deep into my life and helps me chart the right course at all times. Without their having challenged me to run the New York City Marathon in 1990 this amazing journey would never have begun. To my brother Neil for always believing in me and offering both love and support.

My in-laws Dennis, Sue, Mike and Mary Beth for being so wonderful and helping to keep me so grounded. Without you daily life would be so much harder.

To my nephews Quinn and Cameron, my nieces Shea and Catherine... I love you guys and finally, thanks to Mom and Dad for your continued love and support.

New Jersey

Mike Stehle and Jim Milkowski for the use of their terrific personal training studio, "The Training Room," allowing me to train and practice what I teach.

To my Jersey Shore "Stinger" athletes, with a special mention to Linda Piff, Mike and Margerie O'Connor, Tom Schaeffer, David Zurheide, Jim Duffe, Muzz Laverty, Joe Donahue, 2004 Olympic triallist Deirdre Brill.

To "Billy the Kid" Kelly - you've been a great student and training partner - make the most of your opportunity to run while you're in college.

To Kate Lavender, for the many hours of editing that you contributed to this project. Best of luck with your running career!

To the New Jersey Road Runners, Jersey Shore and Shore Athletic Running Clubs, for all that you do to promote the sport of running in the Garden State.

California

To my coaches, Marty Kruger, you helped me become a better runner, Greg Brock you took a runner with some talent and maximized that talent beyond his wildest dreams. Your time and patience with me I will always be grateful for, you taught me so much. My training partners Danny Gruber, Javier Naranjo, Al De la Torre, Jose Aispuro, Barb Acosta, Tim Nash, Glenn Seiler, Jimmy Clark, you guys inspired me, trained, sweated, hurt, laughed, raced and dreamed with me. What a journey it was!

To Michael Lawrence whose friendship and running advice always steered me down the right path.

To my former Iron Maidens Women's Running Group co-coach Shan Aguilar Stone and the athletes, you are the best. Coaching you taught me so much about women's running and about trying to become a better coach.

To Rocky Snyder for your wonderful friendship over the years and for allowing me to use the Pleasure Point Fitness Center for hundreds of workouts providing the facility for me to develop and teach my craft both in running and strength-training. Without the support of your publishing company this project may not have found a home.

To the hundreds of athletes in the Golden State that I have coached challenging me to become a better coach and person, especially to Deanna and the late Don Gardiner for inspiring me. Don's daily battle reminded me to reach out and overcome every day. I miss you.

To Anne Cooney whose love and support was essential at a time when I gambled on a switch in careers. Thank you!

To my very first running client and friend Georgia Hamel who took a chance on a rookie coach and helped the journey begin. To Dr's. Tom Smith and Ray Horan for keeping me healthy and on the roads and track.

To the Mizuno Corporation, for all its support over the years, with a special mention to Ron Wayne and Anthony Narcisco.

To the Santa Cruz Track Club and the staff and kids from Soquel and Aptos high schools for letting me share your track for so many years.

Nationwide

To my RunningBuzz.com partners and good friends Eddy and Shawn Hellebuyck who make it so much fun to work each day and allowed me into their world at the very top of running. To Mbarak Hussein, simply one of the great runners of the world and one of my favorite people.

To the Miami Stingers (Ronnie, Judy, Doug, Kathy and Mimi) for allowing me to guide you all towards your running dreams and aspirations.

Thanks to all my excellent photographic models Kathleen, Shea, Cameron, Marybeth, Mike, Jane, Michael and of course three-time Honolulu Marathon champion Mbarak Hussein for your contributions to this project.

Thank you too to Joyce Magee of the Rockland Road Runners who had the patience to proofread this running tome even while she was putting out their club's award-winning newsletter.

Special thanks

I give special thanks and an enormous debt of gratitude to my sister Nicole for the hundreds of hours spent editing, contributing and advising on Run Tall, Run Easy. Quite simply without you this book would still be in rough form on my desk.

Finally, thanks to running...simply the greatest and purest sport in the world!

About The Author

On November 4th 1990 GP (Gerard Pearlberg) ran the New York City Marathon in four hours and 41 minutes. It would prove to be a race that would change his career and his life.

A successful athlete in school, GP was determined to find out why the running of this marathon had been such a difficult challenge. Since that day he has made it his mission to uncover the secrets to moving one's body across the earth with as much efficiency, economy and speed as possible.

Over the next 13 years, although considering himself most athletically suited to middle distance events, GP ran 20 marathons including a 2:34 at the 1998 Napa Valley Marathon. In the 1998 Nike World Games, GP won the gold medal in the 1500 meters for the 35-39 year age group and ran a 4.21 minute road mile and a 4.01 minute 1500 meters on the track.

GP returned to the New York Marathon in 1996, this time running a 2.42. His unique research on running biomechanics and the fascinating lessons that led to his having shaved nearly two hours off his previous New York Marathon time are shared with you here in *Run Tall Run Easy*.

GP has been coaching professionally since 1995 and has been a (Level 2) USA Track & Field Coach since January 1997. He has coached, counseled, listened to and learned from hundreds of runners, both professional and amateur, all across the United States and South America. He was cofounder of the Iron Maidens all women's running group in Santa Cruz, California and is currently the cofounder of the online coaching company RunningBuzz.com.

Born and raised in England, GP now lives with his wife, Kathleen, his son, Luke and their two dogs on the Jersey Shore, NJ USA. GP and Kathy are expecting their second child in September 2004. GP continues to compete as a Masters runner.

*The author (pictured right) preparing one of
his athletes, Chris Hayes, for competition on
the track in Los Gatos, CA.*

Quick order form:

To purchase a copy or copies of Run Tall, Run Easy -- the Ultimate Guide to Better Running Mechanics, please choose from
the following options.

Order online: Run Tall, Run Easy can be ordered via
www.runningbuzz.com. A printable mail applica-
tion is also available at this site.

Regular Mail: Please include the following information:

Name: _____

Address: _____

City: _____

State/Prov   _____

Zip/Postal   _____

Country   _____

Tel. (optional)   _____

Email (optional)   _____

Along with check or money order to:

Great Performance Coaching and Conditioning
310 Green Avenue
Brielle, NJ 08730
U.S.A

U.S.A. $14.95 plus $4 for shipping, $2 for shipping each additional book.

Intl: $14.95 plus $9 for shipping, $5 for shipping each additional book.

Sales Tax :   *Please add 6% ($0.90) for books shipped to New
Jersey addresses.*

Delivery: *Please allow 3-5 weeks.*

Running notes:

_____
_____
_____
_____
_____
_____
_____
_____
_____
_____
_____
_____
_____
_____
_____
_____
_____
_____
_____
_____
_____
_____

Run tall. Foot strike. Arm drive. Breathing.

Running notes:

_____

_____

_____

_____

_____

_____

_____

_____

_____

_____

_____

_____

_____

_____

_____

_____

_____

_____

_____

_____

_____

_____

_____

_____

Run tall. Foot strike. Arm drive. Breathing.

Running notes:

_____
_____
_____
_____
_____
_____
_____
_____
_____
_____
_____
_____
_____
_____
_____
_____
_____
_____
_____
_____
_____
_____
_____
_____

Run tall. Foot strike. Arm drive. Breathing.

Running notes:

_____

_____

_____

_____

_____

_____

_____

_____

_____

_____

_____

_____

_____

_____

_____

_____

_____

_____

_____

_____

_____

_____

_____

_____

Run tall. Foot strike. Arm drive. Breathing.

Running notes:

Run tall. Foot strike. Arm drive. Breathing.

Running notes:

_____
_____
_____
_____
_____
_____
_____
_____
_____
_____
_____
_____
_____
_____
_____
_____
_____
_____
_____
_____
_____
_____

Run tall. Foot strike. Arm drive. Breathing.

Here is what an American running legend has to say about Run Tall, Run Easy -- The Ultimate Guide to Better Running Mechanics...

"Coach GP has done it again!

I've seen him at running expos around the country talking to people about *Run Tall, Run Easy*. Now with it all in one book it makes it that much easier for people to Run Tall Run Easy all the time!

Written in a form that even the beginning runner will understand, I'm sure that runners of every caliber from casual to world class will benefit from this wonderful book!

I'm now 48 years old and I'm running taller and easier than I have in years! It has re-energized my running! A must read for all runners!"

-- **Dick Beardsley**
Fourth-fastest U.S. Marathoner of all time.
(1982 Boston Marathon 2:08:54)